Tyne & Wear Vol II

Edited by Sarah Marshall

First published in Great Britain in 2005 by:
Young Writers
Remus House
Coltsfoot Drive
Peterborough
PE2 9JX
Telephone: 01733 890066
Website: www.youngwriters.co.uk

SB ISBN 1 84602 232 0

Foreword

Young Writers was established in 1991 and has been passionately devoted to the promotion of reading and writing in children and young adults ever since. The quest continues today. Young Writers remains as committed to the fostering of burgeoning poetic and literary talent as ever.

This year's Young Writers competition has proven as vibrant and dynamic as ever and we are delighted to present a showcase of the best poetry from across the UK. Each poem has been carefully selected from a wealth of *Playground Poets* entries before ultimately being published in this, our thirteenth primary school poetry series.

Once again, we have been supremely impressed by the overall high quality of the entries we have received. The imagination, energy and creativity which has gone into each young writer's entry made choosing the best poems a challenging and often difficult but ultimately hugely rewarding task - the general high standard of the work submitted amply vindicating this opportunity to bring their poetry to a larger appreciative audience.

We sincerely hope you are pleased with our final selection and that you will enjoy *Playground Poets Tyne & Wear Vol II* for many years to come.

Contents

Our Lady Queen Of Peace RC Primary School

Wharrier Street Primary School

The Poems

A Dog's Life

This is the best thing
That a dirty dog could have;
A hot bubbly bath.

This is the best thing
That a happy dog could have;
A big fluffy toy.

This is the best thing
That a pretty dog could have;
A lovely pink bow.

This is the best thing
That a scary dog could have;
A big spiky lead.

This is the best thing
That a playful dog could have;
A blue skipping rope.

This is the best thing
That a posh, proud dog could have;
A blue denim coat.

This is the best thing
That a sleepy dog could have;
A cosy basket.

Philip Jobling (9)
Benton Park Primary School

Anger

Anger is red like a raging fire
It feels like five heaps of garbage in a pile
It tastes like three hundred tabs put in your mouth
It smells like mouldy cheese everywhere I go
It looks like a spicy curry.

Mathew Telford (9)
Benton Park Primary School

A Dog's Life

This is the best thing
That a dirty dog could have;
A hot bubbly bath.

This is the best thing
That a funny dog could have;
A funky toy.

This is the best thing
That a greedy dog could have;
A juicy bone.

This is the best thing
That a tough dog could have;
A spiky collar.

This is the best thing
That a good dog could have;
A flying saucer.

Lewis Foo (9)
Benton Park Primary School

Weather

Monday it is sunny
Tuesday it is cloudy
Wednesday it is raining
Thursday it is frosty
Friday it is snowy

The sun is bright yellow like a ball
A cloud is dark grey and is like smoke
The rain is dark blue and it feels like a wave hitting you
Frost is bright white and very cold
Snow is also cold and white.

Luis Dickie (8)
Benton Park Primary School

In My Garden

Lots of roses
Lots of daisies
Lots of bluebells
Lots of posies
And that's what's in my garden.

Collecting snails
Watching butterflies
Looking at birds in my birdbath
And that's what I see in my garden.

Blackbirds, robins, magpies and starlings chirping in my garden.

Cats meowing
Children screaming
My brother playing football
And that's what I hear in my garden.

Rachel Hodges (9)
Benton Park Primary School

A Dog's Life

This is the best thing
That a dirty dog could have;
A hot bubbly bath.

This is the best thing
That a sleepy dog could have;
A very warm bed.

This is the best thing
That a nervous dog could have;
Someone that loves him.

This is the best thing
That a greedy dog could have;
One whole piece of meat.

Kirsty Moloney (9)
Benton Park Primary School

The Four Seasons

The wind blew,
Rushing and running
In the park when the trees blew
On a cold spring day.

The sun rose,
Slowly and carefully
In the fields
On a lazy summer day.

The leaves fell,
Fast and carefully
At the park where the pond is
On a fun autumn day.

The snow fell,
Sparkling and soft
In a lovely forest
On a lovely winter day.

Georgia Hamilton (8)
Benton Park Primary School

Holidays

I'm going on holiday to have some fun
Jetting off to Turkey to be in the sun.
Splashing in the pool
Wearing my new swimming shorts which are totally cool.
I'm in the water park.
Painted on the wall is a shark.
Lying in the lazy river
I see a huge ride which makes my knees quiver.
My holiday is now at its end
With another school year round the bend.
As I'm coming back home
I will have to wait till next year for my new summer of fun.

Adam Stoker (9)
Benton Park Primary School

Ghosts They Frighten

Ghosts they frighten, ghosts they scare
Playing games upon the stairs
Seeking people all alone
In the bedroom, they're at home.

In the graveyard the moon shines bright
Upon the graves no ghosts tonight
All the people who were once there
Have all disappeared with the midnight air.

Melanie Todd (9)
Benton Park Primary School

Happiness

Happiness is the colour of orange and yellow.
Happiness feels good.
Happiness looks like Newcastle United winning the FA Cup Final.
Happiness sounds like the crowd roaring at a football match
When Supermac smacks the winning goal in from the half-way line
for Newcastle United.
Happiness reminds me of when my mam and dad got married.
Happiness tastes like sweet strawberries on my tongue.

Liam Reynolds (9)
Benton Park Primary School

Happiness

Happiness is the colour of the sun.
It tastes like a fresh melon.
It smells like a lovely flower opening its petals.
Happiness looks like a beautiful bird singing its song.
It sounds like a whole country singing your favourite song beautifully.
Happiness feels like a fawn just learning how to walk.

Christine Burr (8)
Benton Park Primary School

A Dog's Life

This is the best thing that a friendly dog could have;
Other dogs to meet.
This is the best thing that a happy dog could have;
A big chewy ball.
This is the best thing that a furry dog could have;
A soft bed.
This is the best thing that a soft dog could have;
A big plant to chew on.

Hannah Walker (9)
Benton Park Primary School

Weather

Weather so sunny
Ever so warm
Always changing
Thunder then storm
Heat wave and lightning
Emerge in the sky
Rain suddenly splashing by.

Sarah Jobling (9)
Benton Park Primary School

Anger

Anger is the colour brown like a dark old cabinet.
It tastes like smelly garbage.
It smells like green beans.
It looks like rotten cabbage.
It sounds like a growling dog.
It feels like clenched fists.

Stacey Phillips (8)
Benton Park Primary School

The Four Seasons

The sun shone
Wildly and shining
In the colourful sky
On a burning spring day.

The wind blew
Rapidly and wildly
In the green park
On a cold summer day.

The leaves fell
Gently and slowly
Off the old trees
On a cold autumn day.

The snow fell
Strongly and fast
On the white, glistening fields
On a cold, freezing winter day.

Liam O'Connell-Cook (8)
Benton Park Primary School

I Like Noise . . .

The rattle of the rain.
The toot of the train.
The really bad bang of thunder!
The loud moo of the cows.
The jingle of the bell.
The thud of the books falling to the floor.
The flip-flop of the shoe.
The crunch of the cereal.
The pitter-patter of the shower on the windows.
I like noise.

Robert Keegan (8)
Benton Park Primary School

The Four Seasons

The wind was blowing,
Breezy and cold
In the trees
On a beautiful spring day.

The sun shone,
Glittery and sparkly
In the pretty sky
On a lovely summer day.

The leaves fell
Windy and breezy
In the air
On a fun autumn day.

The snow was cold,
White and small
In the cold air
On a fun winter's day.

Paris Dempster (8)
Benton Park Primary School

I Like Noise . . .

The plop of the tap.
The splash of the puddle.
The toot of the train.
The bang of the thunder.
The purr of the cat.
The quack of the duck.
The moo of the cow.
The knock at the door.
The pitter-patter of the rain.
The jingle of the bells.
I like noise.

Jessica Hardy (8)
Benton Park Primary School

The Four Seasons

The wind blew,
Softly and sparkly,
On the warm beach,
On a warm spring day.

The sun shone,
Brightly and warmly,
On the green hill,
On a hot summer day.

The leaves fell,
Glistening and waving,
Off the branch
On a cold autumn day.

The snow fell,
Floating in the sky,
Coming down very white,
On a fun winter day.

Anika Choudhury (7)
Benton Park Primary School

I Like Noise . . .

The plop of a tap in the bath.
The flutter of a bat's wing.
The splash of a puddle.
The squelch of jumping in the mud.
The loud bang of the balloon.
The hoot of the owl at night.
The slam of the door.
The crack of an egg.
The thud of a book on the floor.
I like noise!

Israa Ali (8)
Benton Park Primary School

The Four Seasons

The flowers grew,
Slowly and colourful,
On the bright green hills,
On a miserable spring day.

The sun rose,
Slowly and golden,
In the hot desert,
On a peaceful summer day.

The thunder boomed,
Scary and threatening,
In the dark night sky,
On a scary autumn day.

The hedgehog hibernated,
Curling and nesting,
At the side of the street,
On a white winter day.

Rory Davidson (8)
Benton Park Primary School

Alliteration Poem

Beautiful butterfly bouncing,
Perfect ponies pouncing,
Raging rabbits running,
Cute colts cantering,
Frisky fillies following,
Funny foals fidgeting,
Mad mares munching,
Super stallions swimming,
Silly Shetlands stamping,
Fabulous Fallabellas fighting.

Amy Stocks (10)
Benton Park Primary School

The Four Seasons

The sun shone
Bright and clear
On top of a hill
On a summer day.

The rains fell
Heavily and noisily
On top of a mountain
On a wet spring day.

The snow blew,
Hard and cold
On the top of a cliff
On a horrible winter day.

The leaves blew
Gentle and soft
In a park
On a soft autumn day.

Sean Martin (8)
Benton Park Primary School

Alliteration

Crazy Catherine clinging
Naughty Nicola's nibbling
Naive Naomi's navigating
Evil Emma's eating
Calling Claire's cackling
Eager Ella's earning
Happy Harriet's helping
Bad Ben's bouncing
Terrible Tom's trumpeting
Smelly Sam's smiling.

Hester Alderman (10)
Benton Park Primary School

The Four Seasons

The snow frosted
Sparkling and glistening,
In the cold streets
On a frozen day.

The leaves fell
Slowly and crushed,
In an orange forest
On a warm autumn day.

The wind blew
Calm and whistling,
In the fine lands
On a nice spring day.

The sun shone
Golden and sparkling,
In the fine skies
On a hot summer day.

Liam Owers (8)
Benton Park Primary School

Alliteration Poem

Crazy cats chewing
Dopey dogs dancing
Fantastic foals flying
Happy horses hunting
Prancing ponies partying
Dazzling dolphins diving
Beautiful butterflies bouncing
Reckless rabbits running
Karate kittens kicking
Handsome hamsters hiding.

Jade Smith (10)
Benton Park Primary School

The Four Seasons

The sun shone
Sparkly and beautifully,
In the sunny beach
On a lovely summer day.

The leaves fell
Nice and slowly
In the grassy hills
On a fun autumn day.

The snow fell
Gently and softly,
In the icy hills
On a gorgeous winter day.

The wind blew
Round and round,
On the park, down the hills
On a cold spring day.

Nasiha Shahed (8)
Benton Park Primary School

The Tiger That Died

Once I saw a tiger
At the zoo, bright orange
And pitch-black stripes
I didn't have a clue.

Its cage was small
It did not have enough meat
Its eyes sulked with fear
Of being beaten with a bar.

The tiger cried and then died without a fight
Silently, quietly, quick with delight
I shouted and screamed but I was too late.

Robert Reid (10)
Benton Park Primary School

The Bear's Feelings

I don't care if I am alone!
I still don't care
I'm just in bed crying
And it's just not fair.

The golden sunshine is here
I have to stamp!
I am very angry
They have gone out for a camp!

Help please; I want them to stay here
I am not scared
It's like spooky and dark
Hurry up! I am going to get red.

Ahhh! Finally they are here
It's so calm now
What was that noise?
Oh it's only a cat, 'Miaow!'

Tahrina Tarek (10)
Benton Park Primary School

Lightning

There is a sound you can hear
That may fill your stomach with fear
It is louder than loud
It's from up in the clouds.

A flash of light to us all
Something that's not very small
In my opinion it is exciting
The thrilling sound of lightning.

Andrew Fleming (11)
Benton Park Primary School

The Mountain Bear

I was a very strong bear
Until I got whipped with a bar
I am hurt
At night they lock me in the car.

I get chained up and don't get fed
It is very hot in the summer heat
I don't like it here, I want to go home
I especially don't like my dusty feet.

My fur is starting to burn, it's getting so hot
I wish someone could help me
I hope someone will come quickly
I want to be free.

I'm in really bad agony
And I'm getting really sleepy
People have been laughing at me
People are getting really peepy and peep in my cage.

Rebecca Storey (10)
Benton Park Primary School

Sweets

Lots of sweets that are round
Very posh ones; one for a pound
Some are in the shape of goats
Chew bars that are flavoured with oats
Wine gums, pastilles, suck sweets galore
Starbursts, Skittles I just want more!
I love sweets that you can chew
Guzzle sweets secretly on the loo
If I've got the money I'll buy them old or new!
Whether it's Bassets or Rowntrees I don't really care
I've had all the flavours come grape, come pear
I'll eat all the tuck shop; I'll win all the races
Munching on sherbet or sugar laces!

Patrick Sowter (10)
Benton Park Primary School

The Penguin Who Couldn't Swim

Once there was a penguin who couldn't swim
He tried all day, he tried all night
He hit himself and forced himself
He ended up in lots of fights.

He felt very tired and very irate
All he wished to do was to just swim
He went back home to wash himself
And came back to meet Tim.

Tim said, 'Jump in the water and don't be scared
And kick your arms and legs,
Push yourself off the ice
And you will float like Greg.'

So he took Tim's advice and jumped into the water
He kicked his arms and legs and he pushed himself off the ice
He was very scared
And he swam like a dice.

The penguin was very pleased,
He jumped with joy, he went home
And had a party
And was alone.

Daniel Wright (10)
Benton Park Primary School

Teamism

T his hatred should stop
E xtraordinary things are beginning to pop
A xe so lethal because hate is in people using it as a weapon
M ature people become immature
I t kicks hatred out of football
S underland shouldn't be hated
M en and women bring hatred.

Oliver de Vera (11)
Benton Park Primary School

The Dog

I was playing with my ball
In the back
With my friend
I said, 'Pardon?'

My friend is a girl
Her name is Leah
She is nice
I call her Beah.

My ball is small
It is yellow
We play with it
I call it Pellow.

I am Ball
I am skinny
I am black and white
People call me Mini.

I go in the house
I lie in my basket
I eat my dog food
I am feeling fantastic.

Abbie Duncan (10)
Benton Park Primary School

I Like Noise . . .

The buzz of a bee.
The plop of a raindrop.
The hoot of an owl.
The moo of a cow.
The toot of a train.
The crash of a car.
The knock at a door.
The purr of a cat.

Lauren Thoburn (8)
Benton Park Primary School

How Can I?

How can I put a sock in it if they are on my feet?
How can I lend a hand if I have got them on my arm?
How can I get a shower we're at B&Q?
How can I break a leg if I haven't got a bike?

Samantha Paterson (7)
Benton Park Primary School

How Can I?

How can I go on my bike
When I haven't got my bike with me?

How can I hop on the bus
When I can't reach the top?

How can I break my leg
When my legs are already breaking?

Kyle Mitchell (8)
Benton Park Primary School

Fear

Fear is the colour of red.
It tastes like hot chilli peppers.
It looks like burning hot lava.
It smells like thick smoke.
It sounds like a dinosaur roaring.
It feels like hot ash.

Ryan Bayne
Benton Park Primary School

Happiness

Happiness is the colour of light blue.
Happiness is the taste of roasting hot chicken.
Happiness is the smell of red-hot chips.
Happiness looks like mountains of ice cream.
Happiness sounds like dancing music.
Happiness feels like scoring a goal.

Matthew McCarthy (8)
Benton Park Primary School

Happiness

Happiness is the colour green.
It stands for new life.
It tastes of sherbet lemon.
It smells of lovely daffodils.
It looks like a newborn baby.
It sounds like children playing games.
It feels like a little lamb.

Elspeth Alderman (8)
Benton Park Primary School

Happiness

It is the colour of light yellow and orange.
It tastes like chocolate pudding.
It smells like a bunch of flowers.
It looks like a newborn baby.
It sounds like birds singing.
It feels like a silky dress.

Katie Lackenby (8)
Benton Park Primary School

Happiness

Happiness is the colour yellow
It tastes like sweets
It smells like flowers
It looks like lots of smiley faces
It sounds like lots of children laughing
It feels like smooth sand.

Daniella Forster (9)
Benton Park Primary School

Sadness

Sadness is dark green like a bush in the shade.
It tastes like hot water dribbling down your chin.
It smells like a rotten apple.
It looks like a cold, rainy day when everyone is shivering.
Sadness feels like rain tapping on a rooftop.
Sadness feels like our eyes filling up with tears.

Georgia Hall (8)
Benton Park Primary School

Courage

Courage is a camouflage colour.
It tastes like chewing gum.
It smells like liniment.
It looks like green water.
It sounds like guns banging.
It feels like a rock.

Josh Conlon (8)
Benton Park Primary School

Sadness

Sadness is as blue as the sky.
It tastes like green peas.
It smells like the sea.
It looks like a dark day with rain and lightning.
It sounds like thunder crashing.
It feels like a wet handkerchief.

Claire Davey (8)
Benton Park Primary School

Sadness

Sadness is like a dark-grey cloud.
It tastes like raw egg.
It smells like dying things.
It looks like dark clouds in the sky.
It sounds like lightning.
It feels like being alone.

Cameron Smith (8)
Benton Park Primary School

Courage

Courage is camouflage colours.
It tastes like strong mint.
It smells like mint sauce.
It looks like a battleground.
It sounds like shells screaming.
It feels like a grenade in your hand.

Matthew White (8)
Benton Park Primary School

Classroom Chaos

A is for Allan who picks his nose,
B is for Belza who plays with his toes,
C is for Candler who shouts real loud,
D is for David who's in the science crowd.
E is for Ethan who never smiles,
F is for Fred who works piles and piles,
G is for Gengis who lives over here,
H is for Hannah who really loves beer,
I is for Inti who always does think,
J is for Jessica whose favourite colour is pink,
K is for Katie who is a bit small,
L is for Louise who is *very* tall,
M is for Melissa who made up this poem,
N is for Natalie who lives in a dome,
O is for Ollie who runs a bit slow,
P is for Patrick who loves the snow,
Q is for the Queen who's very, very posh,
R is for Ryan who's friends with Josh,
S is for Sarah who's really cheeky,
T is for Tina who's really sneaky,
U is for Uranus whose favourite colour's green,
V is for Vicky who's really mean,
W is for William who loves his food,
X is for Xanthia who is nothing but good,
Y is for Yoko who commits a crime,
Z is for Zoë who is covered with slime!
My classmates are *so* weird!

Melissa Dean (11)
Benton Park Primary School

An Alphabet Poem

A is for Ashley who never ties her shoes,
B is for Bill who never goes to the loo,
C is for Charlotte who likes to laugh,
D is for Daniel who likes a giraffe,
E is for Ellie who's rather smelly,
F is for Fed who likes jelly,
G is for Gary who likes a snail,
H is for Hester who looks like a whale,
I is for Intisaar who picks his nose,
J is for Jade who likes to do shows,
K is for Katie who's always neat,
L is for Louise who always eats,
M is for Melissa who never lies
N is for Nidea who never cries,
O is for Oliver who's always proud,
P is for Peter who's always loud,
Q is for Queenie who has a lot of passion,
R is for Rose who has a lot of fashion,
S is for Sophie who gets in a mood,
T is for Tony who is a real dude,
U is for Uvin who doesn't wash her hair,
V is for Vina who doesn't share,
W is for Will who thinks he's cool,
X is for Xrina who never misses school,
Y is for Yvin whose got a mum who's mad,
Z is for Zina who hasn't got a dad.

Jessica May (10)
Benton Park Primary School

Alphabet Poem

A is for Anne her face is like a pan
B is for Ben I don't think he's a man
C is for Cathy she never has a laugh
D is for Dan he uses the path
E is for Ellen she's like a melon
F is for Frankie he's always telling
G is for George he thinks he's the king
H is for Helen she's a ming
I is for Izzy her hair is so frizzy
J is for John he's always dizzy
K is for Khan he's not a man
L is for Louise she shops at Topman
M is for Myles he never smiles
N is for Nathan he does not like Myles
O is for Oliver who hates Mrs Ball
P is for Paul he never grows tall
Q is for Queen he whacks people with pans
R is for Robert he likes a man
S is for Susan who is my mum
T is for Tommy who's scared of his Granny Plum
U is for Ugany who does not have a mammy
V is for Vany who likes Tommy
W is for Willy who takes his Auntie Milly to the doctors
X is for Xatcy who poked us
Y is for Yammy who plays with her mammy
Z is for Zoe who does not like her daddy.

Myles McMullen (11)
Benton Park Primary School

A - Z Poem

A is for Allan who is so cool
B is for Betty who acts the fool
C is for Cuthbert who drinks Carling
D is for David who has a darling
E is for Ethel who is so silly
F is for Freddy who hates chilli
G is for Gilbert who robs banks
H is for Harry who never says thanks
I is for Inti who always needs to go for a stinky
J is for Jacob whose body is really slinky
K is for Kyle who can never smile
L is for Liam who can't dial
M is for Myles who hates toes
N is for Neil who hates the hose
O is for Owen who is so tall
P is for Paula who is so small
Q is for Quentin who likes the dark
R is for Rory who eats the bark
S is for Stewart who likes his car
T is for Tommy who likes the smell of tar
U is for Uranus who wees his pants
V is for Victor who likes to dance
W is for Wilma who likes to camp
X is Xerxes who bought a big lamp
Y is for Yorick who likes the sea
Z is for Zack who eats a pea.

Allan Davidson (11)
Benton Park Primary School

The Elephant

Once there lived a grey elephant
The elephant danced
Into the freezing cold
The elephant wore funny pants

And elephant's friends were back in Africa
And one of the poachers dialled
On the phone
The poacher's called Kyle

The elephant is living in the North Pole
In a car
People make funny faces
I got hit with a bar.

When I dance the people laugh at me
All I wear is funny pants
My pants are polka dot
And I dance a polka dot dance.

Each morning
I get hit with a bar
To wake me up
From the car.

Kyle stood with a cup
And asked for money
The tin cup
It said, 'Help monkey.'

Everyday I get chained up
All I want to do is cry
I always get hit with a bar
Everyday I feel like I am going to die.

Connor Mitchell (10)
Benton Park Primary School

Roller Coaster

Roller coaster, when I look at you, you make me cry
When I see people on you
I say to myself how can you go on there?
All I hear is screaming
When I go away from you
My ears are ringing from the screaming.

Claire McDade (11)
Benton Park Primary School

Thought!

I look over the hills,
The gentle breeze fills the air,
I watch and wait
For something unknown
While the flowers sway,
As the sun sets
I stand in the light
As my tears glisten.

Stephanie Holmes (11)
Benton Park Primary School

A Sonnet Of A Favourite Football Team

In the end the home team always collects the ball.
All the time when they play they practically always hit.
When the magnificent team try to score, they fall.
All the glamorous teams never miss as they're attractive and fit.
Most of the time the team scores a lot of spectacular goals.
When you're a football you become very famous and rich.
The team's top striker is called fantastic Mr Scholes.
In schools teachers should teach you all about the pitch.
They play in all weather even in perishing cold.

Amy Cook (11)
Dunn Street Primary School

A Sonnet To The Horse World

Every day all the weather I always go riding
To ride I have to pay a bill
Over jumps, I always go gracefully gliding
All riding takes loads of hard working skill
When riding, keep strong contact on the rubber brown reins
Every year I take lots of complicated tests
The better I am the less the pain
But sometimes it can be a shocking unexpected pest
When cantering gracefully through the huge school
All cute horses get lots of pampering
I find when I am cantering very cool
There are always three bumpy beats in dressage cantering
When putting her head collar on I am leading
At the end of her hard work she's getting her feeding.

Amy Edwards (11)
Dunn Street Primary School

The Sonnet To Andy Cole's Goal!

When the leather spherical hits the smooth post
When it's Saturday on Sky; it's live, exclusive television
We aren't the people really to shout and boast
When I'm in the stadium I have a great vision
When I smacked the globular ball like thunder
When a player has an impressive skill
In the stadium there is always a huge blunder
When it's half-time in the changing room, I chill
When my friend walks through the doors with all the fans
When I used to play for the brilliant Newcastle
Every time Shearer scores there are always roars
There really wasn't that much hassle when I used to play
One brilliant day the one and only Cole
Came to play at Newcastle and scored the winning goal!

Lewis Flynn (10)
Dunn Street Primary School

A Sonnet To Cricket

'Please don't let me down,' said the captain to his winning team
'Go on and play a tough, brilliant match
So play with your heart and follow your dream.
Just close your mouth and use your hands to catch.
Quick, go on and hit that very fast ball
Go quick and get that new willow bat.
Just concentrate so you don't fall.
Just exercise or you will get fat.
Try to hit the ball off the wicket.
You need to be extremely healthy and fit.
Try to score many runs in cricket.
You always have to wear a clean white kit.
It really hurts when you get hit in the shin.
Always try your very, very best to win.'

Jazz Hollins & Jessica Hiscock (10)
Derek Malone & Ashleigh Carr (11)
Dunn Street Primary School

A Sonnet To Andy Cole's Mastermind Goal

When the leather spherical hits the smooth post
When it is Saturday on Sky, live on television
We aren't the first-class people to really boast
There is always such a fearful, beastly collision
When I smacked the globular ball almost like thunder
When the player has an impressive classic stall
There is always in the stadium a huge blunder
In hundreds of homes there is always a glamorous thrill
When he's sprinting like thunder, down the player goes
It is like a journey through a huge cave
Off his golden, amazing fantastical magic toes
When Joe Cole strikes it's a good save
When the ball is smacked fiercely by Andy Cole
What! It is the best masterminded *goal!*

Andrew Martin (11)
Dunn Street Primary School

A Sonnet To A Cat

Big lazy cats are always very fat.
Newborn kittens have tiny little paws.
Mischievous cats slyly run after rats.
Older friendly cats have bigger claws.
Cats are usually cute when they have all their kittens.
When baby kittens are born they're very small.
All baby kittens are as warm and soft as mittens.
Vicious cats are very fierce when they brawl.
Energetic younger cats are very small and fast.
When baby cats wake up their eyes are blurry.
Younger cats are very fast when they run past.
Newborn kittens are not very furry.
Fighting cats are very scary when they wail.
Baby born kittens are often small and pale.

Sophie Joyce (11)
Dunn Street Primary School

Animals And Their Sounds

A night-time creature sings and its name is the lark.
Cute kittens at your feet crying for their mother.
A tiny one man fishing boat being circled by sharks.
An elegant, beautiful, gorgeous dragonfly is starting to hover.
Is that a multicoloured parrot starting that squawking sound?
Squeaky mice are nibbling carefully, quietly at baker's rice.
The cat was chased by the fast fox-hunting hound.
The naughty lice are playing on the red and white dice.
The bird's name is Cheeky Paris, it is a parrot.
I lost Sparky the goldest goldfish on the busy road.
Why is cheeky Lucy eating some white turnips and carrots?
The prickly, spiky, hedgehog got flattened by someone's heavy load.
The baby spotty giraffe has a long, wriggly, twisty neck.
The birds are on my shoulders with my parrot going peck.

Samantha Wildish (11)
Dunn Street Primary School

Sun

Suddenly the rain stops
The magnificent sun is breaking through,
Its hands dragging the gentle clouds away
Burning heat from above has come.

All worries have fled
Because of this wonderful being.
His fingers spread into each street
Spreading light into corners and alleys.

His face like a butterfly
His teeth shine white
And his wonderful smile
Makes the whole world sparkle.

The roar of laughter
Is heard all around
Spring has went
Summer has come.

Jamie Ledger (11)
Fell Dyke Primary School

The Wind

Suddenly the fierce wind is blowing viciously,
Arms spreading the victorious wind,
All around is danger,
Eyes full of anger lighting up like footballs of fire,
A body looking for revenge,
Lashing out,
Hitting everyone in the way,
Destroying and defeating everyone in his path,
Enormous legs leading the blustery wind,
Battling all around the hideous town,
A scream is roaring through the cold air,
Blowing perishing air out into the town.

Gary Watson (11)
Fell Dyke Primary School

Wind

Suddenly the fierce wind blows terribly
As long arms reach out tremendously,
A huge mouth fills up with freezing cold air
Ready to blow again,
People all run as it blows
Darting place to place as it's full of energy,
Furiously crashing into everything,
Quickly the wild wind whistles in the cold air,
As everything then begins to blow,
Starting to destroy things,
Eyes fill up with anger,
A huge roar,
A powerful wind is like a giant in a mood
Furiously blowing people over,
The wind whistles,
Its body moves that fast nobody can see it,
Its body is black, but looks clear,
Then it blows again,
And it then hides away until it is time to come out again.

Rebecca Snowdon (11)
Fell Dyke Primary School

Storm

Suddenly a fierce storm appeared out of nowhere,
Arms of lightning pierced the gloomy sky,
The lightning fuelled by the giant's rage,
Destroying trees and causing blazing fires,
Violent thunder crashed above the silent countryside,
The wind roared and sent an unwanted chill down everyone's spine,
Eyes lit up with anger as the brutal thunder roared violently,
A huge body covered the countryside in darkness,
The darkness was lit up by a blazing flash of lightning,
A bitter wind howled like a wounded giant,
Rain fell heavily from his fingertips
He left huge puddles whenever he stood.

Daniel Glover (11)
Fell Dyke Primary School

Wind

Suddenly the fierce wind howls with anger.
Arms lashing out causing tremendous destruction.
Destroying everything in its path.
Unexpectedly the wind lets out a huge rage.
Whistling with cold, strong breath.
It forces every living thing with unbelievable strength
As it spreads out extreme wind.
People get blown like rag dolls.
As the fingertips touch the soldier's window
A huge roar of wind tries to break it with its determined hands.
Immediately the nails of the fingertips start to scratch
Like terrifying zombies trying to get you.
The wind rushes with tremendous speed around the city.
Suddenly the anger of the wind starts to fade away.
Without a sound it slowly disappears.
As it disappears it lets out a little whoosh.

Sean Poole (11)
Fell Dyke Primary School

Thunder

Suddenly the ferocious storm appears
Defeating the gleaming sun
Powerful arms defeating everything in its way.
Stamping its feet with a loud boom
The jet-black clouds peer at the earth below.
Tears of anger appear,
Lashing out his arms.
A mind full of rage and very bad temper.
He cannot control his temper and his anger.
Powerful muscles emerge as he bangs the clouds together.
His amazing muscles just have to scare the sun away.
A voice roars as it booms very loudly in the dark clouds above.
That it scares everyone off.
Everything turns silent.

Joe Howourth (11)
Fell Dyke Primary School

The Storm

Ferociously, razor-sharp lightning forks
Slash through the stormy clouds,
Arms advance with flames of fury,
Blood-red eyes turn vacant with a sharp glow.
Creating a frighteningly loud boom,
Clashing two enormous cymbals together,
Blowing as hard as possible,
Sounding like a gigantic group of bulls surging towards their enemy.
People tremble to the floor in horror.
Breathing out bitter wind giving people numb fingers,
Chuckling!
Lightning strikes and destroys everything,
Evil mumbles can be heard
As the thunder rumbles
Full of rage and anger.
Floating clouds suddenly turn purple,
Temper is rising,
Bitter shivers trickle down people's spine.
Furious man seeking revenge!
The purple sky is moonless
Giving them a warning,
Multicoloured lightning forks
Endlessly slashing through the earth
Leaving death and destruction.
An angry man weeps unaccompanied.
In dismay people look to see the world demolished.
The calamity has ended,
Surprisingly it gets brighter,
The lifesaver is here.
Jealousy consumes the enraged man,
The defeated man surrenders.

Abbie Paxton (11)
Fell Dyke Primary School

The Storm

Fiercely the raging storm appears out of nowhere.
Blazing eyes burning,
Bulging like red-hot balls of fire.
Arms stretching out to all corners of the world,
Bitter cold and misery is spread about the earth.
On a pale, sagging face, a look of pure, sweet revenge.
Roaring bolts of thunder,
Sending eerie chills down everybody's spine.
Thunder clashes like cymbals,
Breathing freezing winds that destroy everything in their path.
The hurricane will soon be over
Leaving nothing but death and destruction.
Roaring with anger as the rain is poured down,
Flooding the lowly remains of a once happy place.
Lightning forks slash furiously,
Through dismal, grey clouds.
Thinking back to defected pasts,
And sorrowful memories.
With no warning, a blinding light appears from behind a cloud
Commanding the disaster to stop.
At once the ghastly storm comes to a halt.
As though terrified the blizzard cowers.
Disappearing inside a whirlwind in anguish.
The wreck of the world dissolves in a flourish.
The earth is now even more exultant than before.
The sun, the cause of this new-found happiness,
A blinding light appearing from behind a cloud.

Maxine Forster (10)
Fell Dyke Primary School

Thunder

Ferociously the angry thunder clatters down,
Clearing everything in its way.
Its blackened face gazes at everything
Creating ultimate damage on people and cars.
In tremendous pain he strikes the steeple,
That causes a furnace of a fire as he burns in pain,
Leaps out to shock everyone,
You can hear his horrid laugh making everyone shiver,
Its electrifying hair destroys,
Its long gigantic legs and arms strike bolts of fury
Quickly, quickly he moves slaying across the towns,
Putting everything up in flames,
It's like a cheetah struggling in pain fighting for escape.
Suddenly the pain dies and the man and his cheetah got lost
in the demon sky.

Daniel Hare (10)
Fell Dyke Primary School

The Sun

Instantly the cheerful sun comes bursting through the
dreadful black clouds,
Transforming the dull life that lies beneath,
Spreading joy,
Warming up the unpleasant day that is taking place
Filling hearts with fun and laughter,
Dramatically changing the horrific view on earth,
Warm-hearted towards everyone,
Always positive,
Good influence,
Treating everything with respect,
Touching everything with incredibly warm fingers,
Making the horrible atmosphere change suddenly,
Into a delightful place to be.

Stephanie Parker (11)
Fell Dyke Primary School

Wind

Suddenly a whistling wind appeared from behind stillness
With an empty grey face,
He walked miserably through the town,
His arms moving slightly making icy cold winds,
Sending shivers down people's spines.
With a strong breath of bitter cold air
The tremendous howl of the wind got louder.
Just then a giant gasp of freezing cold air went through the town,
Trees started swaying from side to side
And leaves blew down past houses.
Through the night neighbours found it hard to sleep
As perishing cold winds began filling everybody's minds.
But just then the wind was like a fire of wind,
He blew through people's houses
Causing them to wake up feeling chilly.
The wind's fingers spread through the air,
Legs stretched out,
Flying in the air,
Eyes as black as midnight,
You could see the misery in his eyes,
His hair was blowing everywhere in the midnight sky
As he suddenly vanished into the black sky.

Hannah McGregor & Chantelle Cook (11)
Fell Dyke Primary School

The Rain

The heavy rain spits out of the grey clouds,
Fingertips drop sprinkles of rain and sorrow,
Arms gliding quickly through the air,
Legs leading the way leaving puddles of dampness everywhere,
Tapping quietly like a child knocking on a door,
Eyes black and watering with loneliness,
Streets covered in sorrowful, upsetting feelings,
A reflection of a man in the puddles, upset and hurt appears,
An unwanted shiver goes down everyone's spine,
Hair dripping with water as it comes down from the sky,
An insignificant mouth is covered with a gloomy smile,
On the way it makes the earth feel wet and damp,
It clatters on the rooftops and lets everyone know it is there,
People step outside and are tempted to hide,
The strangest feeling emerges,
Why are they avoiding him?
Destiny is lurking as it searches to find it.

Sophie Cooke (10)
Fell Dyke Primary School

Seaside Visit

I could feel the sunlight burning on my skin.
The water felt cold.
I saw some seagulls flying in the air
And I made a sandcastle with my sister Catherine and my friend
Bethany Carter.

Beth Doyle (8)
Our Lady Queen Of Peace RC Primary School

Human Skeleton Dreaming

(Based on 'Fishbones Dreaming' by Michael Sweeney)

Sand trickling falling to the ground,
Touching the tops of every bone.
People shrinking with terror.

This was not her happiest place.
She shut her eyes and dreamt back.

Back to when she was falling,
Being swallowed by the crystal blue sea beneath her,
As the water skimmed close by.

This was not her happiest place.
She shut her eyes and dreamt back.

Back to when the sharks were rampaging through the deep blue sea,
Their sharp teeth gleaming white.
Jellyfish stinging anything in sight.

This is not her happiest place.
She shut her eyes and dreamt back.

Back to when she was roaming freely,
Watching the sea life on the deck of a boat.
The dolphins spinning through the air.

This was her happiest place.
She shut her eyes and dreamt to stay there.

Jasmin Cornish (11)
Our Lady Queen Of Peace RC Primary School

The Beach

Sparkling sun reflecting on the ocean.
Rock pools full of sea creatures.
Children running everywhere full of joy.
The tide going in and out every now and then.
People swimming, paddling and sunbathing.
That is what happened on my trip to the beach.

Joseph Gunby (8)
Our Lady Queen Of Peace RC Primary School

The Girl In The Pit

That poor girl has been woken up at four o'clock in the morning
for the past month.
She was walking along a narrow, quiet path on the way to work.
The coldness of the bucket side and looking up into the
pinhole of light.
She was feeling anxious and worried.
This sound of the pick hammered away at the rock solid coal.
That bitter taste of the coal dust was burning her nostrils.
A vile smell of sweaty, hard-working men was making
her feel queasy.
This rattle of extremely noisy corves got louder and louder
as it approached.
A small candle's light flickered on its last breath.
She was frightened and anxious; she didn't know what was going
to happen to her.
The last of daylight was almost gone when she rose from the tunnel.
That girl was feeling glad she was out of the mine,
But unhappy because she had to go back down again the next day.

Daniel Fittes (10)
Our Lady Queen Of Peace RC Primary School

Seaside

There was the smell of burgers in the air
And shells from the ocean bed nibbling the ocean bed.
Crackling the rocks
Making the sea turtles cry
Making the seals sleep
Making the sun turn the sea light blue
The sound of the seagulls irritated me
There was a loud fair, very big
I could just taste the fish and chip line
And I was in the sunshine.

Jonathan Devlin (8)
Our Lady Queen Of Peace RC Primary School

Tentacles Dreaming

(Based on 'Fishbones Dreaming' by Michael Sweeney)

Tentacles lay on the abandoned seabed.
She was a skull, an eye and a few bony tentacles.
Already she was a nesting place for homeless fish and krill.

She did not like to be this way.
She shut her eye and dreamt back.

Back to her fight to the death with a gnarled sailor
Wriggling and writhing, fighting to resist
The urge to curl up and die
And condemn herself to Davie Jones' watery grave.

She did not like to be this way.
She shut her eye and dreamt back.

Back to when she was being poked and prodded,
Experimented on by men in white coats and rubber gloves.
They were so young yet so evil and she fought to escape.

She did not like to be this way.
She shut her eye and dreamt back.

Back to when her babies were being swallowed up by
The jagged threads of fishing net.
Watching the ugly white ship trundle away with her children in tow.
Crying tears saltier than the sea itself.

She did not like to be this way.
She shut her eye and dreamt back.

Back to when she was a young mother.
Nursing her children and resting.
Watching them play and relaxing in the clear-blue sea.

She liked to be this way.
She dreamt hard to stay there.

Lauren Parkinson (11)
Our Lady Queen Of Peace RC Primary School

In The Coal Mine

Tired when she waits her turn to go down the dangerous bucket
Into the dusty, dirty coal mine.
Last breaths of clean air
Before she steps into the coal mine by the dangerous bucket.
The little flame fading away
When she opens the trapdoor and lets the corves through.
Pain rushing through her head
When she pushes the corves through narrow pathways.
Big clumps of coal heaved into corves and pulled through trapdoors.
Terrible cries of children struggling,
Trying to pull the corves through the water.
The tangled string when she pulls it down
To open the trapdoor and let the corves through.
Rumbles of corves passing through when she picks at the coal face.
Her day has finished and when she gets to the top she feels tired
When she hears she has to do it again she feels even worse.

Lauren Taylor (9)
Our Lady Queen Of Peace RC Primary School

Green

Green is a colour
Green is a mop
Green is a top
Green is a logo
Green is a pogo
Green is a wine glass
Green is a mouldy piece of bread
Green is a smelly shoe
Green is a golden apple hanging on a tree
What else is green . . .?

Soffie Dobinson (9)
Our Lady Queen Of Peace RC Primary School

Life Down The Mine

The pitch-darkness descended down as far as the eye could see.
A scared girl drops into it, fear in her eyes.
Dark outlines of mining men shuffled below working for money.
Corves rumbled through the narrow passageway
Pulled by tired children.
A hard, rugged edge of the coal jutted out, it pierced her skin.
The musty smell of unsettled coal dust burnt her nostrils.
An unbearable smell of sweat from worn-out miners
Picking for lumps of coal
When she sits alone at the trapdoor.
The last shine of daylight as the bucket ascends.
A taste of rotted mould in her mouth torturing her taste buds
When she's alone with the lights out, exhausted - drifting off to sleep.

Matthew Foley (10)
Our Lady Queen Of Peace RC Primary School

A Lost Girl

She is frightened
She is lost
She does not know where to find her mother.

She is too scared
She can't move
She can't move her feet
She is too worried to speak
She is in the woods
She is lost all alone.

Louise Casey (9)
Our Lady Queen Of Peace RC Primary School

Human Skeleton Dreaming

(Based on 'Fishbones Dreaming' by Michael Sweeney)

Human skeleton lay on the
Bottom of the crystal blue sea.
Fish swimming in and out of his head.

He did not like to be this way.
He closed his eyes and dreamt hard back in time.

He thought about being pulled down by the water.
Not being able to breathe, kicking and screaming for air.

He did not like to be this way.
He closed his eyes and dreamt hard back in time.

He thought about hitting the iceberg.
The ship tipping sideways, everyone screaming.

He did not like to be this way.
He closed his eyes and dreamt hard back in time.

He thought about being on the ship,
Before it hit the iceberg, dancing to old love songs.

He liked to be this way.
He closed his eyes and tried to stay like this forever.

Alex Robinson (11)
Our Lady Queen Of Peace RC Primary School

Creepy

Spiders are climbing up the wall,
So scary if they fall, creepy, creepy.
Scorpions are big and crunchy
They make noises on the wall, creepy, creepy.
Snakes are slithery and long, creepy, creepy.

Hannah Telford (9)
Our Lady Queen Of Peace RC Primary School

Life Down The Mine

The pitch-darkness of morning as she had to get up,
She still felt tired.
A cold rusty handle of the bucket made her shiver
As it swayed to and fro.
The blazing lights faded as she descended,
They were going to go out.
This young girl felt very frightened
As she was going in the pitch black.
A hard-working man led her along the mine
To where she was supposed to be.
The young girl now felt hungry,
She had been down the mine for so long.
This girl was a hurrier
With a chain around her waist which was digging into her skin.
There was a big sigh of relief,
She had finished her twelve hour day shift.
The next day, she does it again
Being relieved after each day she finished.

Beth Penny (9)
Our Lady Queen Of Peace RC Primary School

Yellow

Yellow, what is yellow?
Yellow is the sun.
Yellow is the icing on a bun.
Yellow is a mop.
Yellow is a top.
Yellow is a daffodil.
Yellow is the flour from a mill.
Yellow is a logo.
Yellow is a pogo.
Yellow is a book.
Yellow is a cook.
Yellow is a magical colour.
But what else can yellow be?

Chloe Dale (9)
Our Lady Queen Of Peace RC Primary School

A Reason To Cry

She got up at four o'clock feeling tired,
Exhausted and hungry and stumbled out of bed.
Walking miles and miles the day before was horrible.
She had to do it again to get to the mine.
Soon afterwards she was at the entrance.
Her feet were sore and aching.
The last glimmer of daylight was seen
Before the bucket descended into the mine
And then the light was swallowed by the complete darkness.
As the bucket was lowered down it swayed dangerously,
This girl was trying to be brave but she kept sniffling.
The bucket soon come to a stop,
She found herself sitting in a dark, dense room.
She felt the rats biting her feet.
The occasional drip of water was rolling down her face.
This poor girl was feeling tired, miserable and disgusted.
These awful dark rooms made her feel uncomfortable.
After twelve hours of prising the doors open
And letting them bang shut, it was time to go home.
Suddenly her face screwed up and she began to cry
all the way home.

Sarah Riley (10)
Our Lady Queen Of Peace RC Primary School

Swamp

In the swamp there are old trees,
And horrible dull clouds.

It is very strange that I can smell,
Lots of dirty, damp grounds.

There is quicksand in the swamp,
Lots of snakes, what a shame there are no lakes.

I had a dream about a swamp with lots and lots of mud.
I really don't like the swamp and that's why I should.

Amber Cox (8)
Our Lady Queen Of Peace RC Primary School

Crab Bones

(Based on 'Fishbones Dreaming' by Michael Sweeney)

Crab bones lying at the bottom
Of the crystal blue sea.

He did not like this way.
He shut his eyes and dreamt back.

Crab bones watching out for other creatures
Dreaming of when he fought with the fish.

He did not like this way.
He shut his eyes and dreamt back.

He lay at the depths of the sea,
Dreaming of when he was swimming in the deep blue sea
And walking on the shore nipping and biting creatures.

He liked this way.
He shut his eyes and dreamt back to when he was alive.

Bret Scott (11)
Our Lady Queen Of Peace RC Primary School

Baby

I am sleepy and cheeky,
I smile for a while,
I go to Sure Start
We're never, ever apart.

I am happy when my mammy changes my nappy,
I talk while I walk,
I sit in my car seat while sucking my yummy dummy.

I sit in my cot and I laugh a lot,
I cuddle my bears; I have them all in pairs,
My mammy pushes me in my pram.

My mobile sings me to sleep, sometimes I weep,
My mammy changes me in my changer
I act like a Power Ranger,
And that's what I'm like!

Olivia Davison (9)
Our Lady Queen Of Peace RC Primary School

Dolphin Bones Dreaming

(Based on 'Fishbones Dreaming' by Michael Sweeney)

Dolphin bones lay at the depth
Of the crystal blue sea.

She did not want to think this way.
She closed her eyes and dreamt back.

Back to when she was fighting
With the shark.

She did not want to think this way.
She closed her eyes and dreamt back.

Back to when she was floating down to the bottom of the sea
Seeing boats bobbing up and down on the top of the sea.

She did not want to think this way.
She closed her eyes and dreamt back.

Back to when she was jumping in and out of the sea
Watching the sunrise with her friends.

This is the way she liked to be.
She shut her eyes and tried to think that way.

Bethany Allan (11)
Our Lady Queen Of Peace RC Primary School

Seaside Visit

I was visiting the seaside one day,
It was really hot in the month of May.
I could hear the whistling of the sea,
I could feel the stones in the golden sand.
I saw a beautiful, gleaming seahorse under the sparkling,
salty, blue sea.
The seahorse was blue, red, purple and yellow with glitter on its
blue and red stripes.

Lucy Groark (7)
Our Lady Queen Of Peace RC Primary School

Sunken Bones

(Based on 'Fishbones Dreaming' by Michael Sweeney)

Sitting on the crystal blue seabed,
Jagged rocks falling
Off seaweed covered cliffs.

He was not in his happy place.
He dreamt on.

He dreamed to when sharks
With teeth gleaming white
Were chasing him through the ocean.

He was not in his happy place.
He dreamt on.

He dreamed to when he was
Racing through the ocean.
Other fish of his kind were with him.

He was happy in that place.
He tried to stay there.

Aidan Warren (11)
Our Lady Queen Of Peace RC Primary School

Swamp

In the swamp there are lots of old trees,
And horrible dull clouds.
It is very strange that I can smell lots of dirty, damp grounds.

There is quicksand in the swamp and also lots of snakes
It is a very big shame that there are no lakes.

I had a dream about a swamp
It had too many spiders.

Sara Mence (9)
Our Lady Queen Of Peace RC Primary School

Shark's Life

(Based on 'Fishbones Dreaming' by Michael Sweeney)

He lies there without a soul, with only memories left.
He was a shark, a noble great white too.
He had no comfort except the warmth of the Indian Ocean.

He did not want to be this way.
He closed his eyes and thought back.

Back to when he was being chased by poachers through the corals.
He knew so well that he called home.

He did not want to be this way.
He closed his eyes and thought back.

Back to when he was hunting for trout,
Darting through crystal blue waters.

He wanted to stay this way.
He tried hard to stay there.

Taylor McPartlin (10)
Our Lady Queen Of Peace RC Primary School

The Coal Mine

Four o'clock when Lotte had been awoken
She silently went to get her breakfast
She had soggy bread and tiredly she travelled to the mine on foot.
There she climbed into the freezing bucket and was slowly lowered
Down into the darkness constantly swaying side to side.
A noise was getting louder and louder echoing in Lotte's ears.
Lotte was frightened of the bucket; she was frightened of a fall
Which could have paralysed her spine or killed her.
Her sweat had been dripping from her forehead
Thinking of the hard work she was about to do and her
fear of the mine.
Lotte is a trapper and at six o'clock her back breaking is over.
Her fright is gone for a while.

Molly Cairns (10)
Our Lady Queen Of Peace RC Primary School

Working Down The Mine

A glimmer of light as she enters the pit
Feeling extremely scared.
Pitch blankness as she finds her way to the bottom of the pit
Where she can't see at all.
The great rumble of the corf when it enters
As young children pull the mighty wagon.
She hears the sound of children say,
'Hurry up, hurry up, hurry, come in the door with the corf.'
The face of a young child
Who helps her with the job she has.
A rough piece of coal
Scratching her fingers as she loads it into a wagon.
Some horrible stench of mucky coal
Making her nose sore as she works.
The smell of rusty dust going up her nose
Tickling her nostrils, making her want to sneeze.
She feels very scared as she works in the dark all day,
She is afraid of it.
The young girl feels glad she is returning to the surface
But she never wants to go back, even though she has to.

Dominic Old (10)
Our Lady Queen Of Peace RC Primary School

Dancing

You can dance
You can prance
You can be attractive
With your funny outfit
You may be funny
But watch out for
Crocodiles!

Georgia Gow (8)
Our Lady Queen Of Peace RC Primary School

Yu-Gi-Oh

They fight with cards that come alive
You need life points to survive
If you die they get your soul
And trap it in a cage below
There's monsters that are called different names
Magic and traps are just the same
There are forty cards in your deck
The graveyard is a forbidden deck
Having no life points isn't the only way to die
You can run out of cards just like I
Sometimes your duelling can get in a tight spot
Your opponent's cards can destroy the lot
You duel with mats
And that's the last
The game is clever, it plays your mind
You try.

Mark Charlton & Adam Robson (9)
Our Lady Queen Of Peace RC Primary School

What A Dog

I've got a dog,
His name is Perry.
He likes his treats,
And he loves curry.
He likes to bark,
And he plays in the park.
He's never sad,
But he's really mad.
He jumps like a toad,
And he weighs a load.
I love my dog,
Even though he smells like a hog.
He's a dumb dog,
But he's my dumb dog.
What a dog!

Jack Roddam (9)
Our Lady Queen Of Peace RC Primary School

Human Skeleton Dreaming

(Based on 'Fishbones Dreaming' by Michael Sweeney)

A skeleton lay on the dirty seabed.
She, a human, waiting to be found.
Hiding under the crystal blue sea.

She did not enjoy being like this.
She tried to think and dreamt away.

Back to when she was falling downwards.
Closer and closer to the bed of the ocean.
Seeing fish of every colour pass by.

She did not enjoy being like this.
She tried to think and dreamt away.

Back to when she was swimming.
The waves like a mad dog
Swimming out to fetch the ball.

She did not enjoy being like this.
She tried to think and dreamt away.

Back to when she was sunbathing
On the beach with her children
Tim, Claire and her husband Bob.

She enjoyed being this way.
She tried to stay like this.

Jessica Liddle (11)
Our Lady Queen Of Peace RC Primary School

The Seaside Visit

One light evening I went to the beach.
I could hear the seagulls and the waves splashing upon the sand.
I could smell the sea and seaweed.
We took our dogs Ben and Tess
They ran in the sea.
When they came out they were soaking wet.

Faye Muldown (7)
Our Lady Queen Of Peace RC Primary School

Human Skeleton Dreaming

(Based on 'Fishbones Dreaming' by Michael Sweeney)

Human skeleton sprawled on the seabed
With seaweed around him like bars of a prison cell.

This wasn't the way he wanted to be.
He shut his eyes and dreamt his way back.

Back to the time when he was kicking for breath,
A fish swimming up and up,
Then falling down and down into the crystal blue depths.

This wasn't the way he wanted to be.
He shut his eyes and dreamt his way back.

Back to the time when he was on a ship tilting on its side.
People around him mad as maniacs
Sharks beneath him with teeth gleaming white.

This wasn't the way he wanted to be.
He shut his eyes and dreamt his way back.

Back to the time when he was roaming freely on a ship.
On a luxurious cruise soaring out to sea.
Acrobatic dolphins leaping like scissors cutting through
bright, blue paper.

This was the way he wanted to be.
He shut his eyes and tried to stay there.

Amy Groark (10)
Our Lady Queen Of Peace RC Primary School

The Seaside Visit

The smell of burgers in the air
And the shells in the sand
And the seaweed in the sea.
The boys, girls, women and the men,
They are all playing together.
The sea dashing
That's what makes a beach.

Seamus Emery (7)
Our Lady Queen Of Peace RC Primary School

Dreaming Back To The Day Skeleton Was Happy

(Based on 'Fishbones Dreaming' by Michael Sweeney)

Skeleton at the bottom of the golden seabed.
Just a pile of bones,
Soon the fish and sharks would eat him.

He did not like this.
He dreamt back.

Back to when he was on the beach in a dark, tiny hole
Until the tide came in and swallowed him.
Under crystal, clear, blue sea until he was no longer bones.

He did not like this.
He dreamt back.

Back to when he was going to the beach with his family
To see the beautiful shore,
Until the car went out of control straight into the sea.

He did not like this.
He dreamt back.

Back to when he was with his family and friends
Having a laugh and playing with his children.

He liked this.
He thought about it forever.

Jordan Agnew (11)
Our Lady Queen Of Peace RC Primary School

Seaside Visit

I went to the beach and this is what it felt like.
I could feel the sunlight.
I could smell the sea.
I could taste the salt in the sea.
I could hear the seagulls flying above my head.
I could feel the breeze.
I could feel the waves crashing upon my feet.

Shannon Burnhope (8)
Our Lady Queen Of Peace RC Primary School

Going Down The Dark Mine

Her stomach was aching as she pulled the corf forward.
The dirty taste of water going down her thirsty mouth.
The burning smell of candle wax melting away in the pitch-darkness.
The sound of people's footsteps moving every single step
down the coal face.
The weight of the rusty chains pulling her body as she moves along.
The light flickering in the pitch-darkness as she enters down the mine
in the wooden bucket.
The screams of people getting whipped because they haven't done
their job properly.
The sound of dripping water bouncing off the black ground.
The cuts and bruises on her body because she had to get on her
hands and knees and pull.
The taste of horrible dust making her do a terrible sneeze.

Liam Bell (10)
Our Lady Queen Of Peace RC Primary School

My Family

My family is crazy

My dad thinks he's twenty
With his spiked up hair

My mam thinks she's fat
But really she's skinny.

My brother the smallest
He'd like to be the tallest

But me I'm not crazy
Just them

My family is crazy.

Laura Canaval (9)
Our Lady Queen Of Peace RC Primary School

In The Jungle

In the jungle there are
Bees that fly around
Spiders on the ground
Tigers snarl
Lions growl
Scorpions kill
Monkeys thrill
Apes are big
Pandas eat twigs
Snakes can strangle
People gamble
If they go into the jungle
Sometimes trees tumble
Baby buffalo.

Christopher Plumb (9)
Our Lady Queen Of Peace RC Primary School

Baby Baby

I am sleepy and cheeky
I smile for a while
I go to Sure Start
We're never apart.
I am happy when my mummy changes my nappy
I talk while I walk about nothing.
I sit in my car seat while sucking my yummy dummy.
I sit in my cot and I laugh a lot.
I cuddle my bears
I have them in pairs and my mummy pushes me in my pram.
That's about Baby.

Amy Cowley (9)
Our Lady Queen Of Peace RC Primary School

Skeleton Dreaming

(Based on 'Fishbones Dreaming' by Michael Sweeney)

A human skeleton lying on the sandy seabed,
With a head, pelvis, spine, pair of arms and legs.
Soon the enormous seabed would cover him with sand.

He did not like it this way.
He dreamt back.

Back to when he was in the shipwreck.
Sharks circling the boat and colliding,
Into every side of the boat.

He did not like it this way.
He dreamt back.

Back to when he was dining in the ship,
When a sudden crash was heard every one panicked,
Security called over the screams telling everyone to calm down.

He did not like it this way.
He dreamt back.

Back to when he was with his children and wife,
At the seaside on a blazing sunny day.
Holding Alex in his arms, his three month baby.

This was a happy thought.
He kept dreaming of happier times.

Adam Goodyear (10)
Our Lady Queen Of Peace RC Primary School

Spooky House

My house is very scary
There are ghosts all around
They make the house smelly and very cold
My house is big and old
People don't like it, they all run away
That's why I love my house.

Matthew Goodyear (9)
Our Lady Queen Of Peace RC Primary School

Human Skeleton Dreaming

(Based on 'Fishbones Dreaming' by Michael Sweeney)

Human skeleton lay on the ocean bed.
Her head, her legs, her arms and bones,
Soon would go all rotten.

She did not like to be this way.
She shut her eyes and dreamt back.

Back to when she was sitting in the rocking chair.
Telling her grandchildren a story that she loved,
But her grandchildren did not like.

She did not like to be this way.
She shut her eyes and dreamt back.

Back to when she was a teenager,
When she was putting all her make-up on,
And playing with her friends.

She did not like to be this way.
She shut her eyes and dreamt back.

To when she was a baby.
She loved playing with her toys.
When her mum fed her baby food.

She liked to be this way.
She wished it to stay this way.

Rebeka Tobin (10)
Our Lady Queen Of Peace RC Primary School

Faye

F aye is my best friend, I play with her,
A brilliant handstand splitter she is,
Y ou are the best friend I could wish for,
E very time you come round I am very happy.

Siana Poulter (8)
Our Lady Queen Of Peace RC Primary School

Bones Of A Dolphin

(Based on 'Fishbones Dreaming' by Michael Sweeney)

Bones of a dolphin under the sea,
Resting sorrowfully in the sunken,
Wrecked, pirate boat.

She did not like to be this way.
She tried to dream back.

Back to when she was puffing
And panting for breath,
Being chased by a rampaging shark.

She did not like to be this way.
She tried to dream back.

Back to when she was hiding
In the swaying, green seaweed
When suddenly appeared a massive, grey shark.

She did not like to be this way.
She tried to dream back.

Back to when she was laughing
Happily with her friends
Playing hide-and-seek.

She loved this way so badly.
She tried to stay like that.

Amie O'Halloran (10)
Our Lady Queen Of Peace RC Primary School

Seaside Visit

Once I was at the beach
I could feel the sunlight
I could smell fish and chips
I could hear the seagulls
I could feel the shells and sand
I could make sandcastles and holes
I was so hot I jumped in the sea.

Alex Chance (8)
Our Lady Queen Of Peace RC Primary School

Life Down The Mine

As she got into the huge wooden bucket
It descended into the mine, it swayed from side to side.
The dark outline of mysterious figures pulled and pushed.
A small glimmer of light from the candle as it faded into darkness.
The rumble of the corf, as it was dragged through the jet black mine.
When a pick ricocheted off the coal it sent a shiver up her spine.
That old tattered piece of string, she tugged.
She had to pull that cold, heavy corf through that awful mine.
In her mouth was a dry, disgusting taste of coal ash
which made her sick.
As she walked through the mine she bumped into dark
mysterious figures.
When she ascended from the mine it was dark,
if she was lucky she would see a speck of light.
She hardly got any sleep because of the pulse of the aches
in her arms and legs.

Daniel Raymond (10)
Our Lady Queen Of Peace RC Primary School

Seaside Visit

I was digging and digging when I found a shell.
Suddenly a crab's head poked out,
I put the shell down as fast as I could
And the crab ran away as fast as a jet.
It suddenly vanished when the wave crashed down,
But I still kept on digging, on and on.
I didn't notice water coming from the hole.
I kept digging, on and on.
Then I noticed some water coming from the hole.
I stopped digging and built a sandcastle next to the hole.

Arjun Thayyil (8)
Our Lady Queen Of Peace RC Primary School

Lottie's Job Down The Mine

A look at the light as it fades into the darkness
She feels really scared.
Sharp, rough edges of coal rubbing against her fingers,
While she is reaching the bottom of the mine.
The great rattle, rattle, rattle of the harriers
Pulling the corf along the track.
She gets extremely frightened.
Maybe the creek of the mine doors as they open and close.
Now she is terrified.
Children's faces as they drift past,
With no light to guide them along the track.
Rain running down her neck all the way to her feet
As it fell from the ceiling.
Coal dust just settling on the floor of the mine
As it breaks off the coal.
Men's sweat working its way around the mine.
Now she felt sick.
She felt worried and upset, scared and frightened.
She got really worried when she dropped the big bits of coal.
Then she was wrong.
After twelve hours she finally got to go,
Got a good wash and some food to eat.

Charlotte Rathbone (10)
Our Lady Queen Of Peace RC Primary School

Five A Day

Five a day is all you need,
Eat it in any way,
Five a day is all you need
To keep us big and strong.
Apples, pear and dry apricot too,
Kiwi, pineapple and bananas,
Fruit salad with lemon juice,
My favourite fruit in the world.

Louisa Forster (9)
Our Lady Queen Of Peace RC Primary School

Down In The Mines With Lotty

The brown crispy bucket is terrifying,
It sways from side to side, as it descends down into the mine.
A bright light fading away as she looked up from inside the
dreadful bucket.
Petrified as she was walking in the darkness
Along the dusty path to go and be a hard working harrier.
The cold metal belt as it is strapped to her,
So she could pull the heavy corves.
The tremendous rumbling and thundering of the corves
As they are pulled in by little children.
As Lotty finished her horrible twelve hours work in the mine
She was too tired to bath or eat,
When she felt that she had to go down there again.
She wanted to be at home;
She lay in her logging and thought
She would never go down the mine again.

Sian Terry (10)
Our Lady Queen Of Peace RC Primary School

When I Went To The Beach

When I went to the beach
I saw some bleach.
I made a castle
And I ate a fruit pastel.
My dog Max ran around.
There was a big hound
Who was found.
I got a big ice cream
Then the stars came up
And made it gleam.

James Wetherell (8)
Our Lady Queen Of Peace RC Primary School

The Dreaded Life Of Lotte

A glimmer of light got further and further away from her dirty face.
Lotte swayed side to side in the rusty, rotten old bucket
Ready for total darkness.
She stood still in the cold, dark mine
Watching the little light at the top of the mine disappear.
Lotte saw her last bit of light, when she looked up
When she was in the muddy rotten bucket.
Sharp coal cut the ends of her fingers making them bleed.
She moved along the mine,
Ceilings got lower and lower and dark all around, she was terrified.
Sat at the trapdoors Lotte was worried in case she didn't
do her job correctly.
Her face looked worried as she wobbled to and fro
Up in the dreaded bucket ready for home.
She cried in bed, terrified of the horrible, horrible days to come.

Rebecca Crabb (10)
Our Lady Queen Of Peace RC Primary School

Seaside Visit

Looking at the seaside
Makes me want to get in
Finding all the beautiful shaped shells.
They're not on top of the sand, they're under it.
Bring a bucket, bring a spade
Make a sandcastle with your friend.
It soon becomes dark and we have to go.
Our mum and dad get the buckets and spades.
Trying to get the sand out of my toes, it's ever so uncomfortable.
We beg and beg so that we can stay.
It's not fair, just a bit longer to play.
We get to stay a little bit longer,
Please pray that we will be here tomorrow.

Jessica Cornish (8)
Our Lady Queen Of Peace RC Primary School

Down The Mine

There's a tiny speck of light as the bucket is lowered to the mine.
With the outline of figures, at the bottom.
Then the tat, a tat, tat of the corves coming.
And the squeak of the door as it opens for the truck.
All the oxygen rushing towards the open gap.
When she gets to the coal face,
There are big uneven chunks of coal coming towards her.
With little children pulling it,
Her breaths full of dampness and fumes
That could explode any second.
Lots of people racing for the bucket to stay alive.
She doesn't want to go down the mine ever again.
But she has to,
Too tired to eat and drink.

Jake Galea-Hughes (10)
Our Lady Queen Of Peace RC Primary School

Life In The Pit

The feeling of getting up at four o'clock in the morning
Made her feel tired and weary.
A blood-curdling cry of a small girl free falling from the cold bucket
Made her feel scared.
That dot of light overhead lit the dark, tunnelling abyss.
The dozens of doors blocking her path
Through the narrow walkway made her feel annoyed.
Sitting in the familiar hole with rats scuttling all over
Made her feel secure.
This uncomfortable position made her feel scared
And fearing the night.
Feeling the fresh air outside made her feel happy
But the terror of tomorrow hung in the air.

Luke McArdle (10)
Our Lady Queen Of Peace RC Primary School

The Mine

A small flicker of candlelight was on its last breath.
The light was getting smaller and smaller as the bucket went down into the pitch-black.
Her giant belt slowed her down to a stop.
The rugged edge of the coal grazed her hands which made her feel like she could cry.
Some coal dust burnt the back of her throat.
The sweat of hard working men picking away at the coal made her feel queasy.
Scared in the pitch-black with no one to talk to.
The top of the pit when it hit the coal face.
She was tired and hungry,
She felt like she could curl up and go to sleep.
But by the time she got out of the mine, the daylight was gone.

Cassandra Redmond (10)
Our Lady Queen Of Peace RC Primary School

Down In The Mine

Her heart was pounding fast when she was wound down.
The light had shrunk so small that it was out of sight.
Dark outlines of other miners scurried around the mine.
All of the tunnels dripped with dirty water.
A rumble of a corf as it was hauled past.
The crack of a miner as he chiselled at the coal face.
Another lumpy floor poked out, ripping her skin.
A little puddle of ice-cold water glistened in the tiny flicker of a candle.
The sweat of a miner dribbled down his neck.
A stale smell of coal floated around the mine.
Some dirty water dripped to the unstable ground.

Liam Clarke (9)
Our Lady Queen Of Peace RC Primary School

The Horrors Of The Mine

The extra large wooden bucket gave her splinters as she
descended the mine.
She leaned onto a pile of coal while her eyes adjusted
to the darkness.
This young girl felt frightened of the rattle of the corves as
they drew near.
When she had finally reached the coal face she picked up
The heavy wooden handle of a pick against her aching hands.
It had not even been an hour and she was exhausted
After she had attached the great chained belt.
When she was moving the corves she had to stop with pains
on her forehead.
By the sixth hour she had fallen to the floor
So they had to make her retreat to the splintering bucket
She was relieved to be sent back so early.

Katie Briggs (10)
Our Lady Queen Of Peace RC Primary School

The Sea

The sun was bright on my trip to the beach,
I heard the seagulls going *screech!*
I felt the sand dry upon the land.
I smelt the air it was blowing on my hair!
It was quite a windy day so we set out our towels and lay.
I was paddling in the sea and I heard someone go, *'He! He!'*
I found a smooth shell and the trip was going well.
I was having a picnic on the sand when suddenly I heard a band!
We packed our bags and left the beach.
At home I had to use bleach!
I had fun and also a bun.

Kate Foley & Rebecca Laydon (7)
Our Lady Queen Of Peace RC Primary School

In The Desert

In the desert
My feet are sandy
The desert is roasting hot
I am thirsty like a dog
Snakes
Scorpions
Beetles
All around.

In the desert
There are people, people
Looking for food
People on camels
Trees, strange trees
All around.

Sam Baglee (8)
Our Lady Queen Of Peace RC Primary School

Hard Workers

She woke up every morning feeling shattered
As she entered another day of pain.
Going into that old bashed up bucket must be really scary.
But when you get halfway down all you can see up above is torch light.
Total darkness is all you can look at down the dirty mine
And how the dirt splashes over you when the wagons go past.
Screaming noises off other people who also have pain.
Freezing stones that have come from the mucky ground.
The sweat from the old hard workers,
And that's how tired you get after twelve hours of pain.

Josh Makuch (10)
Our Lady Queen Of Peace RC Primary School

The Beach

On the sparkling sand
On the sparkling beach
On the salty land
The sun is still out of reach.
The shining sea
On the sparkling beach
And buzzing bees.
Where the dog is not on a leash
All is well on the sparkling beach.

Eliot Lingwood (8)
Our Lady Queen Of Peace RC Primary School

My Dog

My dog is big and hairy,
Some people think she is scary,
People call my dog Barker
And my dog's best friend is called Arca.

My dog loves me and
My dog loves tea,
My dog is mostly in bed
And cuddling up with her ted.

James Long (9)
Our Lady Queen Of Peace RC Primary School

Doggie Paddle Beach

Sand between your toes like salt.
Water washing up on your feet.
My dog doing doggie paddles.
Paddling down and getting rocks from the bottom of the ocean.
My dad goes down and gets shells for me,
The seashore coming in every now and then.

Abbi Hutchinson (8)
Our Lady Queen Of Peace RC Primary School

Crystal Blue Death

(Based on 'Fishbones Dreaming' by Michael Sweeney)

Human bones lying on rough seabed.
A broken jigsaw drifting.
Lost forever in darkness.

She hated this place.
She opened her memory and looked back.

Back to when she was falling,
Onto jagged teeth waiting to be feed.
Then suddenly like the swoop of eagles' wings
The crystal blue death that swallowed her whole.

She hated this place.
She opened her memory and looked back.

Back to when she was running on grass,
Laughing and giggling but then
Slipping, falling, falling.

She hated this pace.
She opened her memory and looked back.

Back to when she was picking flowers,
Counting clouds, smiling happily,
In the blazing sun.

She liked this place.
She loved this place and kept it close.

Lauren Allen (11)
Our Lady Queen Of Peace RC Primary School

Skeleton Dreaming

(Based on 'Fishbones Dreaming' by Michael Sweeney)

A skeleton lies on the sandy bed.
She was a head, arms and legs,
Small fish live in her ribs happily weaving in and out.

She did not like it this way.
She closed her eyes and dreamt.

Back to when she was falling,
Falling into the crystal blue water.
She was drifting silently down after the terrible battle.

She did not like it this way.
She closed her eyes and dreamt.

Back to when she was battling the sharks,
Fighting for her life,
Taking her last breath before the plunge.

She did not like it this way.
She closed her eyes and dreamt.

Back to when she was swimming,
Swimming out to sea,
Splashing with her family,
Laughing, smiling and playing.

She liked it this way.
She closed her eyes and enjoyed this glorious memory.

Sarah Clark (11)
Our Lady Queen Of Peace RC Primary School

Human Skeleton Dreaming

(Based on 'Fishbones Dreaming' by Michael Sweeney)

Human bones lying in the sandy ocean.
He was a whole man
And fish would try to eat him.

He hated to be this way.
He shut his eyes and dreamt back.

Back to when he was being eaten on a nice plate.
He was with fish and chips
When a man lifted a fork and knife
About to chop him up.

He hated to be this way.
He shut his eyes and dreamt back.

Back to when he was frozen in a freezer
With trout and the lovely ice cream.
Ice cubes dripping down from the top of the freezer.

He hated to be this way.
He shut his eyes and dreamt back.

Back to when he was normal.
Standing with all of his friends,
Going to work, meeting new people every day.

He loved to be this way.
He tried to stay like that.

Jordan Pickford (11)
Our Lady Queen Of Peace RC Primary School

My Dog Floss

(Based on 'Fishbones Dreaming' by Michael Sweeney)

Floss lay on the golden seabed,
A tail, a backbone and a mouldy head.
Dreaming about her once paradise,
This was not her home.

Floss did not like to be this way.
She dreamt and tried hard to wish back.

Floss dreamt about
The waves clashing,
Her owner calling,
Surrounding Floss with crystal blue death.

Floss did not like to be this way.
She dreamt and tried hard to wish back.

Floss dreamt about sharks circling her
Her heart about to jump out of her mouth.
The golden sand covering her up like an unwrapped parcel.

Floss did not like to be this way.
She dreamt and tried hard to wish back.

Floss dreamt about running through the meadows
Filled with all the colours of the rainbow,
Sitting next to the fire, filling her with warmth and welcome.

Floss wanted this dream to stay.
She dreamt on and tried hard to stay there.

Olivia Stratton (11)
Our Lady Queen Of Peace RC Primary School

Boy Skeleton Dreaming

(Based on 'Fishbones Dreaming' by Michael Sweeney)

A skeleton all bone,
Lay on the deep seabed.

He did not like it this way.
He shut his eyes and dreamt back.

Back to when he was twisting and kicking for air
As the long tentacles pulled him under.

He did not like it this way.
He shut his eyes and dreamt back.

Back to when the octopus just grabbed him
As fish were surrounding his every move
And he was screaming in pain.

He did not like it this way.
He shut his eyes and dreamt back.

Back to when he did not want to go in the sea
Because of the roaring waves and the screeching of the seagulls.

He did not like it this way.
He shut his eyes and dreamt back.

Back to when he was enjoying himself on the beach,
He was playing with his family.

He loved it this way.
He tried to dream hard to stay there.

Sam Telford (11)
Our Lady Queen Of Peace RC Primary School

Human Bones Dreaming

(Based on 'Fishbones Dreaming' by Michael Sweeney)

Human bones lay at the bottom
Of the dark, dank floor -
Alone with fish swimming in and out of him.

He did not want to be this way.
He went further back in his dream.

Some of his skin starting to rot.
Nearly reached the bottom of the deep, dark seabed.

He did not want to be this way.
He went further back in his dream.

Floating at the top of the water,
People still shrieking in a terrified way.

He did not want to be this way.
He went further back in his dream.

Getting attacked by sharks, head bitten off.
People shrieking in fear.

He did not want to be this way.
He went further back in his dream.

Playing at the beach,
Throwing a beach ball and swimming in the sea.

He wanted to be this way.
He tried his best to stay this way.

Melanie Emery (11)
Our Lady Queen Of Peace RC Primary School

Human Bones Dreaming

(Based on 'Fishbones Dreaming' by Michael Sweeney)

Human bones lay on the sandy seabed,
He was just a head, spine and a leg.
Soon the krill and prawn would be in trouble.

He lay there dreaming.
He wanted to be another way.

Back to when he was running on the sinking ship,
Looking for his mother like a crazy chimpanzee.

He lay there dreaming.
He wanted to be another way.

Back to when he was boarding the boat
Slowly, really slowly like a small, slow snail.

He lay there dreaming.
He wanted to be another way.

Back to when he was packing his rather small suitcase
Not wanting to leave.

He lay there dreaming.
He wanted to be another way.

Back to when he was winning
His friends wacky, crazy races.

He wanted to be that way.
He dreamt hard and tried to stay that way.

Dale Neil Hodgkiss (11)
Our Lady Queen Of Peace RC Primary School

Human Bones Dreaming

(Based on 'Fishbones Dreaming' by Michael Sweeney)

Human bones rested on the seabed.
He swayed from side to side,
Rocking, rolling, turning with the current.

He did not like that.
So he dreamt on.

He was sinking.
Sinking to the bottom of the sea.
He landed on chests
Of gold and diamonds.

He did not like that.
So he dreamt on.

He was on his ship
Wrestling the pirates.
Eventually he was tied up
And thrown overboard.

He did not like that.
So he dreamt on.

He was walking
Along the seafront.
He was with his family
Laughing and playing.

He loved that.
So he dreamt on and stayed there.

Jack Renwick (11)
Our Lady Queen Of Peace RC Primary School

Seal Dreams

(Based on 'Fishbones Dreaming' by Michael Sweeney)

Seal bones lying on the seabed,
All alone with no one but shrimps,
They were rummaging in his bones.

He did not like to be this way.
He dreamt back further.

Being chased by a shark.
Up and down, under and over the rocks,
Through the weed and
Under the whales.

He did not like to be this way.
He dreamt back further.

He was lost and could not find the other seals.
They were nowhere to be seen.
He had not seen them for days.
He had nothing but the tiny little fish for company.

He did not like to be this way.
He dreamt back further.

Swimming with the other seals.
Jumping in and out of the water.
With all his friends
Eating a lot of very tasty fish.

He did like to be this way.
He tried to keep that thought.

Adam Holt (11)
Our Lady Queen Of Peace RC Primary School

Skeletons Dreaming

(Based on 'Fishbones Dreaming' by Michael Sweeney)

The skeleton dreaming that she was not there.
Not there with the crabs and the krill
Sleeping in her head.
The sharks circling and watching her.

She did not like to be this way.
She dreamt and wished back,
Back to the days when she lived in paradise.

She was gulping down seawater.
She was drowning almost near death.
She was falling, she was dead!

She did not like to be this way.
She dreamt and wished back,
Back to the days when she lived in paradise.

She was sunbathing on the beach.
The sand was squelching between her toes.
Her back sinking into the sand.
She was red and burnt everywhere.

She did not like to be this way.
She dreamt and wished back,
Back to when she was in paradise.

She was walking and running to meet her friends.
She ran and hugged them.
She was talking and being a normal girl.

She liked to be this way.
She dreamt, wished and tried to stay there.
There, where she was, in paradise.

Stephanie Peacock (11)
Our Lady Queen Of Peace RC Primary School

Skeleton Dreaming

(Based on 'Fishbones Dreaming' by Michael Sweeney)

Skeleton lay on the seabed,
Whilst sharks gushed past him with teeth like stars.

He hated this life.
He dreamt on.

He was on the boat,
When a large wave
Sliced him off the bottom of the boat.

He hated this life.
He dreamt on.

He was at the harbour
Waiting for the boat.

He hated this life.
He dreamt on.

He was sitting on the sofa,
All cosy by the fire,
With a blanket round him,
Because he had a cold.

He hated this life.
He dreamt on.

He was playing with his
Children in the living room.

He loved this life.
He dreamt to keep it this way.

Joseph Curley (10)
Our Lady Queen Of Peace RC Primary School

Human Skeleton Dreaming

(Based on 'Fishbones Dreaming' by Michael Sweeney)

A skeleton lay on a sandy seabed,
Pelvis, spine and a pair of arms and legs.
In a while she would rot away beneath the sand.

She did not enjoy this.
She closed her eyes and dreamt back to the past.

Back to when she was in a boat wreck,
With sharks swimming around the boat,
And colliding into the sides.

She did not enjoy this.
She closed her eyes and dreamt back to the past.

Back to when she was sitting,
In a small boat accompanied by her grandparents,
Missing her parents and brother too much.

She did not enjoy this.
She closed her eyes and dreamt back to the past.

Back to when she was at her grandparents' house.
Eating her cold, lumpy porridge,
Before they would set off on a long tiring journey.

She did not enjoy this.
She closed her eyes and dreamt back to the past.

Back to when she was in her cosy home,
Near her parents, friends and brother,
Sitting on the sofa close together, munching on toffee popcorn.

She enjoyed this.
She closed her eyes and thought about those happy times.

Laura Charlton (11)
Our Lady Queen Of Peace RC Primary School

My Friends

My friends are kind although they are hard to find
They are thoughtful and generous
They care and are fair
They play with toys, sometimes with boys
They giggle, tell secrets and are pleasant and cheerful
They have sleepovers and parties at other people's houses
And stay up late because that's what friends are
I don't think you could live without them!

Alice Pizzey (9)
Our Lady Queen Of Peace RC Primary School

Seasons Poem

Winter is frosty and sparkling.
Winter is cold and snowy.
Winter is when we can make snowmen, angels.

Summer is hot and breezy.
In summer I have a big BBQ!
In summer I have water fights.
In summer I get the paddling pool out.

Spring is bright.
Spring tastes like sweat.
Spring looks like a big light shining.
Spring sounds like baby lambs.

Autumn is when leaves fall off the trees.
Autumn is when pink and brown is around trees.
Autumn is when animals get ready for the cold.
Autumn is when all the conkers fall.

Liam Donaldson (9)
St Anthony's CE Primary School, Newcastle-upon-Tyne

Hopscotch Ten

Hopscotch one and two
Hopscotch three and four
Hopscotch five and six
Hopscotch seven and eight
Hopscotch nine and ten
There is a ghost
Behind you!

Hopscotch one and two
Hopscotch three and four
Hopscotch five and six
Hopscotch seven and eight
Hopscotch nine and ten
There is a bogeyman behind you!

Paige Jamieson (8)
St Anthony's CE Primary School, Newcastle-upon-Tyne

Ready Rabbit Go

Come on let's
Go to the rabbit races
My rabbit will
Beat a pace.
Roland Rat will commentate
And Melony Monkey
Will shoot the gun to start.

All the yogs
Will go, 'Uy, Uy.'
Come on now
The race is starting
Off we go
Bang! Bang!

Litalia Tumilty (8)
St Anthony's CE Primary School, Newcastle-upon-Tyne

School Days

At five to nine
Every class goes to line
At nine o'clock
The gates get locked
At five past nine it's register time
At ten past nine it's assembly time
School days, school days
The best days are Fridays
We're here to work
We're here to play
We're here to have a happy day
At nine thirty
The boys get dirty
They're playing football
But some of them fall
At eleven o'clock
The teachers get a shock
A schoolboy broke an arm
They hope it's not much harm
At twelve o'clock
Pack up your stock
Pick a lunch and get some munch.

Aaron Drummond (11)
St Anthony's CE Primary School, Newcastle-upon-Tyne

Dolphin

D is for diving
O is for play with octopus
L is for a long body
P is for playing
H is for a happy dolphin
I is for intelligent
N is for nature.

Jason Clark (8)
St Anthony's CE Primary School, Newcastle-upon-Tyne

Playground Fun

In the playground you can play everyday.
Under the sky and above the railway.
On the ground you can go skipping,
Play football and even play hissing.
Play tuggy with your friends,
It's better than to play with a pen.
Sing a song, a sweet little tune,
Hear the birds underneath the moon.
Dance and play every single day,
Until you can no more say.

Roberta Jakas (9)
St Anthony's CE Primary School, Newcastle-upon-Tyne

Emotions - Love

Love is happiness.
Love tastes of apples.
Love smells of cauliflower.
Love looks like a rainbow.
Love sounds like a bird.
Love feels like loving somebody.

Samantha Annan (9)
St Anthony's CE Primary School, Newcastle-upon-Tyne

Dogs

D is for the darkness when he lies
O n the mat he likes to lie
G is for googly eyes when he's awake
S is for smooth fur.

Lewis Davies (7)
St Anthony's CE Primary School, Newcastle-upon-Tyne

Emotion - Sadness Is . . .

Sadness is crying.
Sadness is lonely.
Sadness is shouting.
Sadness is tears.
Sadness is hate.
Sadness is black.

Craig McAllister (9)
St Anthony's CE Primary School, Newcastle-upon-Tyne

Emotion Poem

Love is caring.
Love is romantic.
Love is sharing.
Love is nice.
Love is like a big hug.
Love is like a big heart.

Callum Tumilty (9)
St Anthony's CE Primary School, Newcastle-upon-Tyne

Happiness Is . . .

Happiness is visiting my nana.
Happiness is playing football.
Happiness is when I go on holiday.
Happiness is when I go to the town moor.
Happiness is when I go to a football match.
Happiness is when I go out with my dad.
Happiness is when I go out with my nana.
Happiness is when I go to the swimming baths.

Carl Ramel (9)
St Anthony's CE Primary School, Newcastle-upon-Tyne

Playground

In a playground you can play,
In a safe way.
Play tuggy with your friends,
But not with your pens.
Join the football team,
It's really fun,
Have an early playground run.
I found somewhere to play,
It was just like a day.

Enver Kanidagli (10)
St Anthony's CE Primary School, Newcastle-upon-Tyne

My Emotions Poem

Calmness is white and lemon.
Calmness tastes like ice cream.
Calmness looks like a soft fluffy cloud.
Calmness smells of roses.
Calmness sounds like humming in the distance.
Calmness feels like smoothness.

Rachel Nesbitt (8)
St Anthony's CE Primary School, Newcastle-upon-Tyne

My Emotions Poem

Love is red and yellow.
Love tastes of apple.
Love smells of roses.
Love looks like happiness.
Love sounds like a heartbeat.
Love feels like a big hug.

Lauren Hindmarsh (9)
St Anthony's CE Primary School, Newcastle-upon-Tyne

The Perfect Day For Me

Sunny gorgeous day out,
Everyone licking lollies,
Boys playing football,
Girls playing dollies.

Hot lovely day out,
Everyone playing together,
Mums and dads chatting,
And babies playing with a feather.

Mild beautiful day out,
Time to go for tea,
Everyone waves goodbye,
That was the perfect day for me.

Kimberly Straughan (10)
St Anthony's CE Primary School, Newcastle-upon-Tyne

Playground Fun

In the playground you can play,
In a very safe way,
There are so many things to do,
Instead of it just being you,
Play all day with all your friends,
Instead of using plastic pens.
Join the football team it's really fun,
Have an early playtime run.
Sing a tune just like a bird,
It's better then doing your work,
Basketball and football is really good,
Have a fun playtime just like you should.

Cassie Hamilton (9)
St Anthony's CE Primary School, Newcastle-upon-Tyne

Playground Friends

I stand at the school gate,
I talk to my mate.
Some people are on time,
Some people are late.
It's time to play football,
Let us play, we will win,
Let's put my apple in the bin.
People sing and dance,
They've got the chance.
I play headers and volleys,
A man is selling lollies.
Can I go and get one,
Uh oh he's gone
Goal!

David Annan (10)
St Anthony's CE Primary School, Newcastle-upon-Tyne

Playing

I play headers and volleys,
And people move their bodies.
I play basketball,
And some of the players are tall.
I play football,
And I sometimes fall.
I play on the stepping stones,
And I wriggle my blood and bones.
My school mates dance,
They've just got the chance.

I never stop playing tuggy
And I tug people sweetly.

Toni Cooper (10)
St Anthony's CE Primary School, Newcastle-upon-Tyne

Playground

I walked into the school gate
And I went to talk to my best mate
We like to talk about what we did last night
And I said it was great flying my kite
Then Cassie said 'What are we doing today?'
'Dance to Black Eyed Peas,' I say
The bell goes, in we go
But I know I will be back in a minute or so.

Chantelle Orr (10)
St Anthony's CE Primary School, Newcastle-upon-Tyne

My Emotions Poem

Hate is red and black
Hate tastes like porridge
Hate smells of burning
Hate looks like fire
Hate sounds like bullets
Hate feels like rocks.

Lester Drummond (9)
St Anthony's CE Primary School, Newcastle-upon-Tyne

A Dream Of Mine

I wanna go to a disco,
In the fab San Francisco.
I wanna meet a pop star
And drive in a flash car.
I wanna be groovy
And make my own movie.
I wanna buy a top or bag
Or something with a designer tag.
I wanna make some jewellery so fine
With little jewels that always shine,
That would be a dream of mine.

Laura Crutwell (10)
St Gregory's RC JMI Primary School, South Shields

What Will I Be?

When I grow up
What will I be?
A doctor? A dentist?
A cook at sea?

I could write a best selling book
I could paint a famous picture
I could marry a wealthy duke
And make my family richer.

I could be a designer of fashion
I could go to Art College
I could be a business executive
And impress people with my knowledge.

I could be a shopkeeper and stack shelves
I could be a journalist, writing the latest scoops
I would work in a cathedral ringing the bells
I could be a colonel inspecting the troops.

I could be a judge and send prisoners to jail
I could be a scientist and make different potions
I could be a builder and bang in nails
I could be a sea captain and sail the oceans.

I could be an actress and star in famous films
I could be an air stewardess and give people comfort when they fly
I could be a potter and cook plates in kilns
I could even go to Russia and be an undercover spy.

From astronaut to air stewardess
From bartender to biomechanics
From carpenter to car mechanic
I'll always try to do my best and do a good job.

Ellen Smith (10)
St Gregory's RC JMI Primary School, South Shields

Police Life

Being a policeman,
Patrolling on the streets,
Thinking of the people,
You would not like to meet.

Jumping out of bushes,
Giving you a fright,
Walking in the daytime,
Driving round at night.

Look at all these people,
Without you they aren't safe,
They'll clap and cheer as you walk by,
If they see a friendly face.

You're there for them at sunrise,
You're there for them at noon,
You're there for them at night-time,
Bad guys quake at the siren's tune.

So when the day is over,
Forget the work you've done,
When you're resting,
Do not wake . . . until the rise of the sun.

Zofia Bungay (10)
St Gregory's RC JMI Primary School, South Shields

Baby In The House

Baby in the house,
Arrived last week,
Absolutely stinks,
Likes playing hide-and-seek.

Mum and Dad,
Oh, it's not fair,
Always gets attention,
It doesn't care.

All it does is sleep,
Oh maybe eat too,
Screaming, oh it's too much!
Hides then shouts boo!

It's never even you know what trained,
Scribbles in my books,
Just too much!
Pulls our coats off the hooks.

I've never in all my life,
I'm so depressed,
Being trampled on,
I'm being oppressed.

Katherine Hamilton (9)
St Gregory's RC JMI Primary School, South Shields

I Wish I Could Fly

If I could fly,
I would fly high in the sky.
Like a bird I would fly high
In the sky I would swoop and dive.
Oh how I wish I could fly.

If I could fly,
Like a kite I would go high
Far in the night,
I would take flight.
Oh how I wish I could fly.

If I could fly,
High in the sky,
I would fly higher than the
Clouds as they pass by.
Oh how I wish I could fly.

Amy-Jayne Young (8)
St Gregory's RC JMI Primary School, South Shields

The Bully Is Coming

When I go to look in the mirror,
I always face an angry gorilla.
I am so scared like a bird,
That I hear sounds that will be heard.

When I get up and go to school,
You always start to push me into the swimming pool.
My bones feel like breaking apart,
But when the bully comes I always get caught.

My body will be hurting today,
I wish the bully would just go away.
The bully always comes after me,
I am not happy and neither is he.

Stacey Brettwood (9)
Seaburn Dene Primary School

Anger

I see anger in their eyes,
I feel scared when
I go down the street,
I feel depressed inside.

When I look in the mirror,
I think 'Why choose me?'
My friends were shocked at dinnertime.

I start to shake outside
When I go home
I start to cry,
I sigh loudly,
I cry softly.

Sometimes I feel
I was not wanted in this world.
I can't bear it any longer
But why?

Sara Aslam
Seaburn Dene Primary School

The Bully Is Coming

I see the bully standing in front,
My bully standing there is giggling away,
I see the bully and wonder if he's going to punch,
My bully is there and coming my way.

I feel some butterflies whirling around my tummy,
I feel my eyes fluttering out of my body,
I see the bees, but can't hear them humming.
I feel, but don't know if the bully will say sorry.

I wake up and always hear,
The bully's foot standing on my toe,
Inside my body, my tummy, there is fear,
Outside I can hear feelings really sore.

Hannah Curran (9)
Seaburn Dene Primary School

The Person Who Liked Me

I'm the person you did not like
I'm the person who was scared of you
I'm the person you bullied all day
I'm the person who had friends
But they've turned into a person just like you.

I'm the person who felt like jelly
I felt like there was an aeroplane flying inside me
I'm the person who felt like she was melting
Im the person who had butterflies in her belly.

I'm the person who could hear herself screaming
I'm the person who could hear the bully was in my team
I'm the person who could hear the bully saying bad words
I'm the person who could hear the bully in my dream.

Hannah Gough (9)
Seaburn Dene Primary School

The Victim

As I approached the school
There they were waiting for a battle.
I can feel them kicking and punching me.
I feel weak and my bones are jelly.
I feel that I am going to be sick.
I can hear people laughing in my ears.
Everyday my stomach's turning.
I see them every corner I turn.
They pushed me in the stream.

No one to tell.
No one to see.
No one to tell what it's doing to me.
I just want it sorted out.
I am the victim.

James Roper (9)
Seaburn Dene Primary School

The Bully

I can see my son depressed and sad and hurt.
Nothing seems to cheer him up.
It makes me feel so sad.
What can I do to help him?

He's scared to go to school.
He pretends to be sick.
Then he starts to cry.
What can I do to help him?

He comes back with scrapes on his knees.
He runs all the way home.
He goes upstairs and cries in his room.
What can I do to help him?

I can ask him what is wrong.
I can listen to him.
I could put a stop to it.

Jack Randle (9)
Seaburn Dene Primary School

Untitled

I am the victim
I can see people shouting, kicking and pushing
I feel scared, frightened
I feel that people will look at me
My bones feel like jelly
I thought I was going to be sick
I thought that I was going to die
I can hear people staring at me
I can hear enemies following me
I am the victim.

Luke Tulloch (9)
Seaburn Dene Primary School

My Life Is A Disaster

I saw the bully waiting for me at the playground
I saw my friends playing happily all the time
I saw myself in the mirror at the toilets
I dreaded to see the bully's face again
I was so nervous, scared to come out from the toilets
All I could do is cry, cry, cry.

My body was weak and my heart was broken
My bones felt like jelly wobbling all the time
Now playtime's over and I have to come out
But I couldn't face this person again.

I can hear the slap of the bully's hand on my skin
I can hear the teacher say 'Get into partners'
The bully is my partner
My heart is beating fast, faster
That was it, my life was a disaster.

Anna Worthy (9)
Seaburn Dene Primary School

Scared At School

I can see him walking up to me, not anyone, the bully.
He is there - sitting next to me, staring into my eyes.

I can feel kicking, punching all over my body.
I fell down and scraped my knees.
My bones were like jelly.
My head was pounding.

I heard name calling and shouting,
Screaming, crying, whinging and snapping!
But most of all I heard nothing.

Liam Watt (9)
Seaburn Dene Primary School

The Bully Is Coming

I see his eyes full of blazing fire
He treats me like a slave and I treat him like a sire.
He has great big muscles in his legs
He has big, bony arms and eyes as big as fried eggs.
He has jet-black hair and a devilish grin
Every time he pokes me, his finger feels like a pin.

They say your tummy's full of butterflies, but mine is full of snakes
I feel my strength's been drained away by garden rakes.
I'm ashamed I can't stand up to a bully,
After all he's just a person who I can't understand fully.
The bully must feel sad or lonely
He thinks he's cool, but he's a phoney.

I hear the lightning strike the ground every time he takes a step
Every time he doesn't hit me, I'm in great debt.
I hear his hand slapping my face
I hear him laughing at me like I'm a disgrace.

Luke Morris (9)
Seaburn Dene Primary School

I Am The Victim

I stay in my bedroom to get ready for school,
I always try to be cool,
I go to school with nobody.

I wait for the thunder and lightning,
I see the bully trying to be frightening,
Yes, I am the victim.

I am lonely, scared,
Don't know what to do,
Yes, I am the victim.

I hear the hand slapping the bully's fist,
Tears fill my eyes like ponds.
Yes, I am the victim.

Holly Henderson (9)
Seaburn Dene Primary School

Now I'm A Bully Too

He turned into a monster,
Then turned me into one too.
When I look in the mirror,
I see fierce eyes staring back.

Inside my stomach I feel sick,
Then I feel stronger than ever.
When I put my clothes on, it feels nice,
Then I feel sweat in my shoes.

I awake in the morning hearing fists, smashing faces,
I hear footsteps coming.
It is him coming round the corner,
It's time to fight!

Catherine Lamb (9)
Seaburn Dene Primary School

The Victim Is Aware

My friend turned into a bully,
I am the only person who gets up scared,
Only I protect myself on the street,
And I always keep aware.

Every night and day I'm frightened,
I always think of my heart pounding,
I can hear the bully's fist,
And I am always aware.

I can hear the bully slapping me,
And I can hear the bully stomping to my door.
In the playground I never play with anyone,
And I am always aware.

Callum Johnson (9)
Seaburn Dene Primary School

Every Time

Every time I walked to school,
I was petrified because of you,
I tried to hide, but it didn't work,
But then you found me,
Then locked me in the loo.

It was as nasty as it could be,
My tummy felt like it was made out of jelly,
This was nowhere near me,
Petrified and terrified that's me now.

When I wake up, I smell the bully,
Never wanted to go back to school.
The shoes going on my face,
Then the bully tries to drown me in the swimming pool.

Jennifer Wild (9)
Seaburn Dene Primary School

It's Like My Friend Has Rebelled

My best friend is now a bully
And now I am locked in a room not feeling fully.
When I am walking I don't want to be shown
I bet you just want to break one of my bones.

I have feelings just as well
And I can't stand anyone or tell.
It feels like I have butterflies in my tummy
But I bet you think it's cool being a bully.

When I am asleep I hear words like, 'Go to Hell'
It's like my friend has rebelled.
I don't want to eat my food
But I don't feel like being a cool dude!

Megan Souter (8)
Seaburn Dene Primary School

I Saw A Monster

I saw a monster and it attacked
I don't know why, but it changed me,
When I see my friend I see a monster like the first.

But when I look in the mirror I see the monster,
And I close my eyes and feel fear.

My stomach feels like it's full of his scorn,
My legs wobble like jelly.

Every night I can't hear sweet dreams like others
I just hear his fist pound on my face.

Takunda Karima (8)
Seaburn Dene Primary School

The Bully

I see in my dreams the person I most fear,
Who used to be a friend, but now just a peer,
When I go to school I feel petrified
When he sees me I feel like I could die,
The bully has friends who bully me as well,
I suddenly thought it was my parents I had to tell.
I hear deafening screams in my mind,
And I find that they are mine.

Cameron Duell (9)
Seaburn Dene Primary School

A Limerick

There once was a girl called Rose
Who loved to pick her nose
She picked out her brain
It fell down the drain
And that was the end of Rose.

Andrew Brett (9)
Wharrier Street Primary School

World Cup Victory

The crowd screamed,
'Score a goal England!'
The crowd roared as I saved a German shot.

A brilliant game, four-two victory
Losers are Germany
Britain has glory.

Anthony Ions (10)
Wharrier Street Primary School

A Teacher From Wharrier Street

There once was a teacher from Wharrier Street
Who liked eating Shredded Wheat.
And she told everyone
She will meet someone.
His name is Pete
And that is why the teacher from Wharrier Street
Eats Shredded Wheat.

Charlotte Cochrane (9)
Wharrier Street Primary School

There Was A Girl

There was a girl
She loved to twirl
She spun around in her dress
And ended up in a mess
Now she always wears trousers!

Maryanne McDaid (9)
Wharrier Street Primary School

There Once Was A Girl

There once was a girl
Who lived with her sister and mother too
She goes to Wharrier Street
Where she listens in school
She gets a book and reads it
Straight home to do her homework
She is a bright girl
She is always a star
Very nice to everybody
A lovely girl.

Sinead Sproston (10)
Wharrier Street Primary School

World Cup Final

The crowd screamed
As I scored the winning goal
It was like a dream come true.

The crowd screamed
As I saw the last five seconds.
I could not get it out of my mind.

Five . . . four . . . three . . . two . . . one
The whistle went!

James Poole (9)
Wharrier Street Primary School

Mr Copping

There once was a teacher called Copping
Who liked to shout quite often
His throat became sore
He couldn't take it no more
Now he is quiet Mr Copping.

Chellsie Hall (9)
Wharrier Street Primary School

1966 World Cup

The crowd screamed,
'Come on England you can beat Germany,
You can win the World Cup!'
Although the ref got knocked down.
It was half-time, it was one-one
One of the England players scored a hat-trick
The crowd screamed extremely loud
All the England players jumped on one of the players
It was three-one then one of the other players scored
Then it was four-two
They think it's all over. . .
It is now!

Ryan Black (9)
Wharrier Street Primary School

Shipwreck

(Based on a painting by Turner)

Raging
Mysterious
Powerfully destructive
Mystical, misty, ferocious
Darkness.

Steven Watson (11)
Wharrier Street Primary School

The Panda

Slow, sturdy, but steady it climbs,
Up a tree looking for bamboo,
With his strong hands clutched around the tree,
He looks for more bamboo,
Slowly he reaches the top,
Tired.

Ryan Burns (11)
Wharrier Street Primary School

Mrs Bland

Mrs Bland, Mrs Bland
The kindest teacher in the land.
Shout, shout, shout
Mrs Bland, Mrs Bland
The funniest teacher in the land.
Ha, ha, ha!
Mrs Bland, Mrs Bland
The wildest teacher in the land.
Growl, growl, growl!
Mrs Bland.

Darren Mann (9)
Wharrier Street Primary School

Why Do I Have To Go To School?

Why do I have to go to school?
Maths, literacy, science and history.
This is such a mystery.
Why do I have to go to school?
Question marks, exclamation marks.
Why do I have to go to school?
Having to write till late at night.
I guess I need to follow the rules.
That's why I have to go to school.

Jade Chapman (10)
Wharrier Street Primary School

The Sea

Bright sea
Shimmering soft
Golden sparkle shining far away
Sun reflecting light
Twinkle!

Claire Craig (11)
Wharrier Street Primary School

That Was The Day

That was the day,
When my life had just begun,
And I had seen the world for the first time.

That was the day,
Everyone was fussing over me.

That was the day,
I got new things.

That was the day,
I can't remember anymore.

Shiarn Daniels (11)
Wharrier Street Primary School

The Moon

In the dark evening sky it stands,
Looking over our homelands,
Its face so bold and bright,
Illuminates the blue night.

Through passing night it strolls through the stars,
Shining in the sky afar
He starts to move with a smile on his face
Then leaves the night with such grace.

Devan Jamieson (11)
Wharrier Street Primary School

Shipwreck

The waves
Crashing against
The torn oak ship as the
Innocent victims scream in terror
Listen . . .

Zoe Graham (11)
Wharrier Street Primary School

My Thoughts Will Take . . .

In my head is a fantasy dream
Which will take all my bad thoughts.

In my head is a dream catcher
Which will take all my nightmares.

In my head is a big smiley face
Which will take all the evil smirks.

In my head is a sunny day
Which will take all the dark clouds.

Rachel Gilbert (11)
Wharrier Street Primary School

The Moon

A smiling face with deep, black eyes
Shuffling slowly in the sky,
He stares upon us throughout the night,
He holds a secret but won't tell it,
He turns to the stars to whisper it,
They twinkle,
Then he turns back to me and smiles,
The man in the moon is mysterious.

Rachael Ross (11)
Wharrier Street Primary School

Sour Satsuma

Sour Satsuma
Makes me fizz.
Sour Satsuma
She's called Liz.

Georgia Carr (9)
Wharrier Street Primary School

Rainbow

Looking down on us every time
Rain and sun are the sign
Clouds are drifting through the sky
As rainbow gives a heavy sigh
Listens in the daylight drift
The clouds of sky give a lift
Whispers over wondering world
Sun goes dim, rainbow curls.

Victoria Butler (10)
Wharrier Street Primary School

Thoughts

If all my joyful thoughts took shape
They would be like a shimmering sun.

If my miserable thoughts took shape
They would be like a shipwreck at sea.

If my spiteful thoughts took shape
They would be like clouds falling.

If my exciting thoughts took shape
They would be like a beautiful waterfall.

Emma Kirkbride (11)
Wharrier Street Primary School

Motorbike

Single seater
Petrol drinker
Traffic light ignorer
Car beater
Neighbour waker.

Callum Brown (10)
Wharrier Street Primary School

The Moon

Gliding above the troubled world,
He listens carefully to what is heard,
Watching over the evening sky,
Shining brightly way up high.
He protects the stars with golden hands
Shining over wasted lands.
Crawling towards the end of night
He is amazing and so bright.

Amy Ellitson (11)
Wharrier Street Primary School

My Cousins

Troublemakers
Fight starters
Dead leg givers
Mess makers
Argue battlers
Girl hitters
Cheek givers
PlayStation fighters.

Carla Jones (10)
Wharrier Street Primary School

My Dog

Arm biter
Cat catcher
Claws doors
Barks loud at night
Bird eater
Digs holes
Worm eater.

Natalie Larmouth (10)
Wharrier Street Primary School

My Little Sister

Hair puller
Room messer
Aggravator
Water spiller
Night crier
Toy taker
Name caller
Noise maker
Bath splasher.

Connor Woodhead (10)
Wharrier Street Primary School

Thoughts

If my happy thoughts took shape
They would be like a glowing sun.

If my sad thoughts took shape
They would be like a dark, dull day.

If my quiet thoughts took shape
They would be like a scurrying mouse.

If my evil thoughts took shape
They would be like a jagged rock.

David Whitton (11) & Emily Wilde (10)
Wharrier Street Primary School

My Dog

My dog is stinky
My dog runs very quickly
My dog is huffy
He likes clean people.

Samantha Mifsud (10)
Wharrier Street Primary School

Apples Are Round

Apples are round and so red,
Of course, you don't eat them in bed,
Red apples are juicy and so crunchy,
Please, please buy them
Because they're so munchy.

Charlotte Bendelow (9)
Wharrier Street Primary School

Shipwreck

Thunder
Crashing, rumbling
Killing sailors on-board
Taking victims all day
Killing victims.

Ryan Gates (11)
Wharrier Street Primary School

My Dirty Dog

My dog is dirty
It does not like spiteful cats
It loves a good fight.

Conor Barron (10)
Wharrier Street Primary School

The Moon

Strolling wonderfully through the stars,
Clenching the sky with gripping hands.
Looking down on us with his silver eyes
Until the morning arrives.

Steven Atkinson (10)
Wharrier Street Primary School

The River Tyne

T eeming with use
H ealthy and clean
E verywhere is alive.

R iver of dreams
I nsects around
V ery clean
E verything's happy
R ushing clean streams.

T eeming with fish
Y esterday's dirt
N o more to be seen
E verywhere's clean.

Chloe Wright (8)
Wharrier Street Primary School

Birds

B irds are beautiful.
I n the trees, always singing in the summer.
R obins fly so high in the sky.
D oves always sing.
S un is shining on the birds.

Rebecca Snowdon (8)
Wharrier Street Primary School

I Am An Orange

I am an orange
I've got orange hair
I just want to go to the fair
If you don't let me
I'll go up in a flare.

Karl Armstrong (9)
Wharrier Street Primary School

Thoughts

If my good thoughts took shape
They would be the quiet sea.
If my sad thoughts took shape
They would be a war-torn country.
If my terrifying thoughts took shape
They would be a rusty coffin.
If my exciting thoughts took shape
They would be a shining motorbike.

Daniel Mooney (11)
Wharrier Street Primary School

Dolphins

D olphins in the deep blue sea
O pening its mouth, time for tea
L aughing and playing
P icturing a saying
H iding and gliding
I love dolphin riding
N ose as powerful as dragon fire
S enses are very strong like wire.

Jodie Hay (11)
Wharrier Street Primary School

The Panda

With soft white hands,
It grips bamboo shoots.
With clothes of black and white,
It can sleep through the night.
When it stands,
It can see the whole land.

Liam Black (10)
Wharrier Street Primary School

The River Tyne

Rivers and streams blue like the sea.
Fish swimming in the streams.
Used to be dirty, now it's clean.
Teeming with life, healthy and clean.
Everywhere's alive, rivers and streams.
Insects abound in the vegetation.
Everyone's happy, a new generation.
Teeming with fish, yesterday's dirt has gone.
No more to be seen, the Tyne is clean.

Kieren Black (8)
Wharrier Street Primary School

All By Yourself

All by yourself lying in the dark
Creepy as spiders lurking in the park.
Like a baby starting to run
Running along the tram lines
You told me you were having fun.

Damon Robson (11)
Wharrier Street Primary School

Blue Sky

Soft day
Wind blows softly
The sun shines through the clouds
Sun glowing across the blue sky
Peaceful.

Elysha Williams (11)
Wharrier Street Primary School

Birds

Birds can fly up in the sky
When they get hurt they begin to cry
They make their nests with sticks and straw
When I give them food they love me more.
Birds bring happiness, joy and fun
Sometimes they go out and eat a bun
Birds always tweet, tweet, tweet, tweet
And birds are also very sweet.

Shannon Murray (8)
Wharrier Street Primary School

Working

Working is great
Working together we'll get the job done.
I love working, I love working.
You will learn more if you listen.
Working together makes it best.
Games and things and no work at all.
That is what I don't like.
I only like work.

Jermaine Havery (8)
Wharrier Street Primary School

My Own

All on my own leaning against a flower bed,
I am abandoned, just left at the bottom of the ocean,
Embarrassed to be seen by humans,
They would just kick me to pieces and call me old rust
As I try to move my wheels screech,
The flowers complain to me that I squash them
I'm a bike all on my own.

Gemma Child (11)
Wharrier Street Primary School

Birds

B irds fly high
I n the sky
R ound and round they fly
D oves are nice and white
S ome birds like to fight.

Caitlin Stewart (8)
Wharrier Street Primary School

Birds

B irds make their nests in the spring
I t is egg laying time
R eady for their greedy chicks
D o you ever disturb them?
S ome birds lose their eggs because other greedy birds take them.

Ross Wynyard (8)
Wharrier Street Primary School

Birds

B irds are beautiful and they bring happiness.
I n the spring the birds glide in the sky.
R obins are red, they are my favourite birds around.
D oves are lovely, doves are white.
S eagulls are fast, seagulls go and bite.

Stephen Gray (8)
Wharrier Street Primary School

I Want To Paint

I want to paint a train on a track.
I want to paint a sweet in a pack.
I want to paint love in the world
And that's what I want to paint.

Katie Rushford (11)
Wharrier Street Primary School

In My Head

In my head there is
Excitement because I am
Going to the pictures to see
XXX2 with my best friend
Next week.
In my head there is a
Solution to be on a football
Team.
In my head there is
Excitement because I am
Going to Newcastle
Academy in July.

Jason Milor (11)
Wharrier Street Primary School

Summer

S ummer is a brilliant time
U nder the skies so blue
M um tells me to rake the garden
M um sunbathes to get a tan
E verywhere is colourful
R eady for the autumn.

Mia Hicks (8)
Wharrier Street Primary School

Amulet

Inside the wolf's eyes there is an emerald sea.
Inside the emerald sea there is a creature of destruction.
Inside the creature of destruction there is a hurricane.
Inside the hurricane there is a hungry child.
Inside the hungry child there is sadness.

Jamie Taylor (11)
Wharrier Street Primary School

Demons' Heads

Demons buried deep in the ground
Glaring forward wanting to be found
Waiting for a storm to come to reunite with everyone
Snatching thunder, Hell fights below
Awaiting in the darkness, opening the door.
Feeling angry with impatient yells.
Demons arise from their grassy cells.
Through Hell's people can they pass.
They wipe out all with their destructive path.
A lightning flash illuminates an angry sky,
Feeling lonely, hear a chilling cry
From the stones they begin to rise
A creak of stones, a thousand sighs.

Terri Mole & Mathew Gowens (11)
Wharrier Street Primary School

School

School is like a puppy dog.
Welcoming you with its never-ending love.
A friendly face, in a friendly place.
Always ready to greet you.
Never judging whatever you do.
Always ready to meet you.
We can learn together.

Rebecca Mills (10) & Donna Robson (11)
Wharrier Street Primary School

Birds

B irds can fly in the sky
I like birds when they fly.
R eally cool in the sky.
D o all kinds of things in the bushes.
S hining in the pretty blue sky.

Shannon Kellie (8)
Wharrier Street Primary School

School Of Rock

School is over,
Oh what fun.
Lessons finished.
Play begun.
Who will run fastest?
You or I?
Who will laugh loudest?
Let us try.

Jasmine Whitlie, Alishya Lister & Katie Rushford (11)
Wharrier Street Primary School

Shipwreck

(Based on the painting by Turner)

Darkness
Mysterious
Powerful waves pouncing
Ravaging everything in sight
Deadly.

Scott Atkinson (10)
Wharrier Street Primary School

Dragon Rocks

Sculptures of dragons,
The rough grass itching.
Wanting to come back alive
So they can save their family.
Helping and loving the one they love
Dragons.

Nicole Mole (11)
Wharrier Street Primary School

The River Tyne

T eeming with life
H ealthy and clean
E verywhere's alive.

R iver of dreams
I nsects around
V ery clean
E verything's happy
R ushing, clean streams.

T eeming with fish
Y esterday's dirt
N o more to be seen
E verywhere's clean.

Jack Stobbart, Kyle Mannion, Ryan Dale,
Josh Lawson, Chloe Wright & Karl Kildare (8)
Wharrier Street Primary School

Birds - Theme

Big birds, small birds, all shapes and sizes
They all have their own disguises
My favourite is the robin
Robins are gorgeous
I love their colours too
Watch out for them in your garden
Christmas will soon be coming.

Chloe Russell (8)
Wharrier Street Primary School

1966 World Cup

The crowd screamed
When they scored the first goal
Then we came back with some smashing goals
We scored again
That got us to four-two.
My team was so nervous
To see the Queen.
When I got back home
I was amazed to see how
Many people were there.
We were so happy to win the World Cup
And I was just happy to get to bed.

Ben Daniels (10)
Wharrier Street Primary School

Thoughts

If my happy thoughts took shape
They would be like a glowing sun.
If my sad thoughts took shape
They would be like a dark dull day.
If my quiet thoughts took shape
They would be like a scurrying mouse.
If my evil thoughts took shape
They would be like jagged rocks.
If my exciting thoughts took shape
They would be like a horse cantering.
If my lovely thoughts took shape
They would be like a mum giving me a cuddle.

Sophie Shears (11)
Wharrier Street Primary School